# CALIFORNIA

## McDougal Littell

# MATH

### Course 1

**Larson    Boswell    Kanold    Stiff**

## Practice Workbook

The Practice Workbook provides additional practice for every lesson in the textbook. The workbook covers essential skills as well as problem solving. Space is provided for students to show their work. Answers to the Practice Workbook exercises are provided on the interleaf pages of the Teacher's Edition and in the Chapter Resource Books.

**McDougal Littell**

A DIVISION OF HOUGHTON MIFFLIN COMPANY

Evanston, Illinois  •  Boston  •  Dallas

# Contents

**Chapter**

# Program Overview

Pupil
Edition

**eEdition**
CD-ROM and online

Teacher's
Edition

Resource Manager

**Activity Generator**

**Power Presentations:
The Electronic Classroom**
with animations

**Easy Planner**
DVD-ROM

Best Practices
Toolkit

English
Learner
Package

Workbooks

- **Practice Workbook**
  (English and Spanish)
- **Notetaking Guide**
- **California Standards
  Review and Practice**

Assessment
and
Intervention

**eWorkbook
ClassZone**

**Test Generator**
CD-ROM

**California @Home Tutor**
CD-ROM and online

McDougal
Littell
Assessment
System

ClassZone

# Practice Workbook Overview

**The Practice Workbook provides additional practice for the lessons in the textbook that includes:**

- Skill practice
- Problem solving practice
- Space for students to show their work

Name _____     Date _____

**Write all the factors of the number.**

**1.** 29              **2.** 63              **3.** 70

**4.** 34              **5.** 120             **6.** 66

**Tell whether the number is *prime* or *composite*. Explain your reasoning.**

**7.** 98              **8.** 41              **9.** 57

**10.** 59             **11.** 73             **12.** 25

**13.** Describe and correct the
error in writing the prime
factorization of 56.

$$56$$
$$8 \quad \times \quad 7$$
$$2 \quad \times \quad 4 \quad \times \quad 7$$

**Complete the factor tree.**

**14.**              **15.**              **16.**

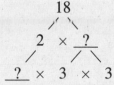
18
2 × ?
? × 3 × 3

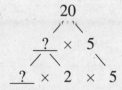
20
? × 5
? × 2 × 5

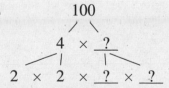
100
4 × ?
2 × 2 × ? × ?

## LESSON 1.1

# Practice continued

For use with pages 5–9

**Use a factor tree to write the prime factorization of the number.**

**17.** 72

**18.** 125

**19.** 44

**20.** 95

**21.** 156

**22.** 77

**23.** You are planning to put a tile border along a 126-inch-wide wall in your kitchen. You want to use only whole tiles. List all the possible whole number tile widths you could use. If the tiles are only sold in whole number widths of 6 inches or less, what size tiles could you use?

**24.** You are putting up a 90-foot-long fence in your backyard. According to the manufacturer's instructions, the fence posts should be equally spaced along the length of the yard. List all the possible spacing options if the amount of space between the posts is a whole number of feet. If the posts should be spaced between 8 feet and 14 feet apart, how far apart should your posts be?

Name _____    Date _____

# Practice

For use with pages 10–14

**Find the greatest common factor of the numbers by listing factors.**

**1.** 42, 90            **2.** 34, 68            **3.** 56, 150

**4.** 28, 45            **5.** 60, 350            **6.** 40, 68

**Find the greatest common factor of the numbers using prime factorization.**

**7.** 30, 135            **8.** 45, 56            **9.** 99, 165

**10.** 132, 198            **11.** 20, 88, 165            **12.** 168, 180, 450

**13.** What is the greatest common divisor of 135 and 450?

    **A.** 5            **B.** 15            **C.** 25            **D.** 45

**14.** Describe and correct the error in finding the greatest common factor of 60 and 126.

    Factors of 60: 1, 2, 3, 4, 5, 6, 10, 12, 15, 20, 30, 60

    Factors of 126: 1, 2, 3, 6, 7, 9, 14, 18, 21, 42, 63, 126

The greatest common factor of 60 and 126 is $2 \times 3 \times 6 = 36$.

**15.** The greatest common factor of two numbers is 5. What could the two numbers be?

**LESSON 1.2**

# Practice *continued*
### For use with pages 10–14

16. You made 63 wheat dinner rolls, 45 rye dinner rolls, and 54 sourdough dinner rolls for a family picnic. You want to make up plates of rolls to set on the picnic tables. If each plate is to contain the same amount of each type of roll, and there are no leftover rolls, what is the greatest number of plates that can be made? How many wheat dinner rolls, rye dinner rolls, and sourdough dinner rolls are on each plate?

17. A college class with 30 sophomores, 18 juniors, and 12 seniors is divided into project groups where each group has the same number of sophomores, juniors, and seniors. What is the greatest number of groups that can be formed? How many sophomores, juniors, and seniors are in each project group?

18. A piece of paper is 280 millimeters long and 200 millimeters wide. You want to draw a grid on the paper so that there is a whole number of squares on the paper. What are the possible sizes of the squares? What is the largest possible square?

**Practice**
For use with pages 15–20

**Match the equivalent fractions.**

1. $\frac{8}{12}$

2. $\frac{4}{5}$

3. $\frac{6}{8}$

4. $\frac{4}{9}$

A. $\frac{24}{30}$

B. $\frac{24}{54}$

C. $\frac{10}{15}$

D. $\frac{42}{56}$

**Write two fractions that are equivalent to the given fraction.**

5. $\frac{28}{44}$

6. $\frac{42}{60}$

7. $\frac{45}{90}$

**Write the fraction in simplest form. Graph the number on a number line.**

8. $\frac{22}{66}$

9. $\frac{42}{105}$

10. $\frac{78}{90}$

11. $\frac{24}{48}$

12. $\frac{54}{60}$

13. $\frac{51}{68}$

**Write the fractions in simplest form. Tell whether they are equivalent.**

14. $\frac{4}{14}, \frac{10}{35}$

15. $\frac{60}{96}, \frac{35}{56}$

16. $\frac{25}{40}, \frac{60}{84}$

17. $\frac{40}{70}, \frac{36}{60}$

18. $\frac{36}{39}, \frac{72}{78}$

19. $\frac{60}{132}, \frac{48}{88}$

Lesson 1.3

**20.** You have completed 32 problems of history homework and you have 16 problems left. What fraction of the problems have you completed? Write the fraction in simplest form.

**21.** You are on a road trip and make a rest stop after being on the road for 85 miles. You have another 55 miles to go until you reach your destination. What fraction of the trip have you completed? Write the fraction in simplest form.

**22.** A bag of 24 balloons contains 16 yellow balloons. A larger bag of 50 balloons contains 33 yellow balloons. For each bag of balloons, write a fraction in simplest form comparing the number of yellow balloons to the total number of balloons. Are the fractions equivalent?

*Lesson 1.3*

Name _____ Date _____

**Find the first three common multiples of the numbers by listing multiples.**

**1.** 9, 12          **2.** 5, 14          **3.** 12, 16

**4.** 15, 20          **5.** 4, 9, 12          **6.** 8, 9, 24

**Find the LCM of the numbers using prime factorization.**

**7.** 42, 126          **8.** 75, 105          **9.** 54, 210

**10.** 30, 50          **11.** 72, 108          **12.** 8, 30, 45

**Find the GCF and the LCM of the numbers using prime factorization.**

**13.** 18, 20          **14.** 60, 72          **15.** 56, 84

**16.** 12, 27          **17.** 16, 63, 75          **18.** 36, 60, 135

**19.** Describe and correct the error in finding the least common multiple of 8 and 60.

$$8 = 2 \times 2 \times 2$$
$$60 = 2 \times 2 \times 3 \times 5$$
$$2 \times 2 \times 3 \times 5 = 60$$

So, the LCM of 8 and 60 is 60.

# Practice *continued*
For use with pages 21–25

**20.** Which two number pairs have the same LCM?

    **A.** 3, 16         **B.** 4, 14             **C.** 6, 8             **D.** 8, 12

## Find the LCM of the denominators of the fractions.

**21.** $\frac{1}{3}, \frac{1}{2}$                 **22.** $\frac{2}{5}, \frac{1}{8}$                 **23.** $\frac{1}{2}, \frac{5}{6}$

**24.** During the summer, you mow lawns for extra money. One customer pays you to mow the lawn every 6 days and another customer pays you to mow the lawn every 9 days. If you mow both lawns today, in how many days will you mow both lawns again on the same day? If today is Monday, on what day of the week will you mow both lawns again on the same day?

**25.** At an animal rehabilitation center, the baby rabbits need to be fed every 8 hours and the baby squirrels need to be fed every 6 hours. If the rabbits and squirrels are both fed at 9:30 A.M., when will they be fed again at the same time?

**LESSON 1.5 Practice**
For use with pages 27–33

**Complete the statement using $<$, $>$, or $=$. Check using a number line.**

**1.** $\frac{3}{4}$ ___?___ $\frac{9}{16}$

**2.** $\frac{3}{5}$ ___?___ $\frac{7}{8}$

**3.** $\frac{2}{9}$ ___?___ $\frac{7}{15}$

**4.** $\frac{7}{12}$ ___?___ $\frac{5}{18}$

**5.** $\frac{5}{8}$ ___?___ $\frac{15}{24}$

**6.** $\frac{12}{35}$ ___?___ $\frac{2}{5}$

**7.** Which fraction is between $\frac{3}{5}$ and $\frac{3}{4}$ ?

**A.** $\frac{11}{20}$          **B.** $\frac{12}{15}$          **C.** $\frac{34}{40}$          **D.** $\frac{8}{11}$

**Order the fractions from least to greatest. Graph the numbers on a number line.**

**8.** $\frac{3}{4}, \frac{5}{48}, \frac{3}{8}, \frac{5}{6}$

**9.** $\frac{4}{5}, \frac{5}{8}, \frac{11}{20}, \frac{3}{10}$

**10.** $\frac{8}{9}, \frac{2}{3}, \frac{10}{27}, \frac{15}{18}$

**11.** $\frac{3}{4}, \frac{11}{24}, \frac{13}{18}, \frac{8}{9}$

**12.** $\frac{4}{15}, \frac{7}{12}, \frac{4}{5}, \frac{23}{30}$

**13.** $\frac{11}{15}, \frac{7}{18}, \frac{3}{5}, \frac{5}{9}$

**Compare to $\frac{1}{2}$ to tell which fraction is greater.**

**14.** $\frac{5}{12}, \frac{17}{30}$

**15.** $\frac{11}{24}, \frac{29}{35}$

**16.** $\frac{13}{30}, \frac{25}{41}$

Name ——————————————————————————— Date ———————————————

**17.** $\dfrac{14}{28}, \dfrac{21}{54}$

**18.** $\dfrac{65}{130}, \dfrac{40}{75}$

**19.** $\dfrac{31}{55}, \dfrac{52}{110}$

**20.** In 2005, 48 out of 80 members of New Jersey's House of Representatives were Democrats and 27 out of 60 members of Oregon's House of Representatives were Democrats. For each state, write a fraction for the number of Democrats in the House to the total number of House members. Which state had a greater fraction of Democrats in its House of Representatives?

**21.** In the recently completed season, a baseball player got a hit 70 times out of the 254 times he was at bat. In the previous season, the player got a hit 50 times out of the 210 times he was at bat. For each season, write a fraction for the number of hits to the total number of times at bat. In which season was the ball hit a greater fraction of the time?

Name _____  Date _____

**LESSON 1.6** **Practice**
For use with pages 35–39

CA Standards
NS 1.1

**Write the mixed number as an improper fraction.**

1. $4\frac{1}{4}$

2. $3\frac{2}{3}$

3. $2\frac{6}{7}$

4. $5\frac{4}{9}$

5. $6\frac{3}{10}$

6. $8\frac{2}{15}$

**Write the improper fraction as a mixed number. Graph the number on a number line.**

7. $\frac{11}{2}$

8. $\frac{15}{4}$

9. $\frac{53}{10}$

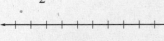

10. $\frac{23}{3}$

11. $\frac{51}{11}$

12. $\frac{53}{16}$

13. Describe and correct the error in writing $5\frac{4}{9}$ as an improper fraction.

$$5\frac{4}{9} = \frac{5 \times 4 + 9}{9} = \frac{29}{9}$$

14. Which number is between $\frac{34}{9}$ and $3\frac{8}{9}$?

A. $3\frac{7}{9}$

B. $3\frac{5}{6}$

C. $3\frac{5}{9}$

D. $\frac{31}{9}$

**LESSON 1.6** 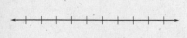 **Practice** *continued*
For use with pages 35–39

**Order the numbers from least to greatest. Graph the numbers on a number line.**

**15.** $2\frac{2}{5}, \frac{11}{5}, 2\frac{3}{10}, \frac{31}{10}$

**16.** $4\frac{1}{2}, \frac{19}{4}, \frac{37}{8}, 4\frac{3}{16}$

**17.** $\frac{23}{3}, 7\frac{4}{9}, \frac{55}{9}, 7\frac{5}{18}$

**18.** $4\frac{11}{24}, 5\frac{1}{4}, \frac{31}{6}, \frac{57}{12}$

**19.** $1\frac{3}{4}, 2\frac{2}{5}, \frac{21}{10}, \frac{29}{20}$

**20.** $9\frac{1}{6}, 10\frac{1}{4}, \frac{61}{6}, \frac{83}{9}$

**21.** A recipe for whole-wheat bread calls for $2\frac{1}{4}$ cups of flour. If you only have a one-fourth cup measure, how many one-fourth cups of flour do you need?

**22.** The top four discus throws at a track meet are $97\frac{1}{8}$ feet, $97\frac{3}{5}$ feet, $97\frac{1}{4}$ feet, and $97\frac{2}{9}$ feet. Order the numbers from least to greatest. What is the distance of the longest throw?

**LESSON 1.7** **Practice**
For use with pages 40–46

**Match the number with its point on the number line.**

1. $2\frac{7}{8}$     2. $2.65$     3. $2.\overline{4}$     4. $\frac{61}{20}$

```
        A   B   C   D
  ←―+―+―+―+―●―+―●―+―●―+―●―+―+→
   2.0  2.2  2.4  2.6  2.8  3.0  3.2
```

**Write the fraction or mixed number as a decimal.
Then tell whether the decimal is a _terminating decimal_
or a _repeating decimal_.**

5. $\frac{2}{5}$     6. $\frac{8}{3}$     7. $5\frac{3}{4}$     8. $4\frac{2}{9}$

**Rewrite the repeating decimal using bar notation.**

9. $0.4444\ldots$     10. $2.161616\ldots$     11. $3.67777\ldots$

**Write the decimal as a fraction or mixed number.**

12  $0.6$     13. $0.18$     14. $3.25$

15. $1.375$     16. $0.125$     17. $6.34$

**Compare the statement using $<$, $>$ or $=$.**

18. $1.25 \underline{\ ?\ } 1\frac{3}{8}$     19. $2\frac{5}{6} \underline{\ ?\ } 2.8\overline{3}$     20. $3\frac{5}{11} \underline{\ ?\ } 3.45$

Lesson 1.7

**LESSON 1.7**

# Practice continued
For use with pages 40–46

**Order the numbers from least to greatest.**

**21.** $\frac{2}{5}, 0.34, \frac{7}{3}, 0.3, 0.\overline{3}$

**22.** $\frac{23}{4}, 5.65, 5\frac{4}{5}, 5.\overline{6}$

**23.** $\frac{23}{20}, 1\frac{1}{5}, 1.01, 1.\overline{15}$

**24.** At 31.04 miles, the English Channel Tunnel is one of the world's longest railway tunnels. Write the length as an improper fraction and as a mixed number.

**25.** In 1991, Mike Powell set the men's long jump world record with a jump of $29\frac{3}{8}$ feet. Write the distance as an improper fraction and as a decimal.

**26.** In the United States, the five Great Lakes cover an area of 94,710 square miles. The smallest of the Great Lakes, Lake Ontario, covers an area of 7540 square miles. Write a fraction in simplest form that compares the area of Lake Ontario to the total area of all the Great Lakes. Then write the fraction as a decimal to the nearest hundredth.

Lesson 1.7

## LESSON 1.8 Practice

For use with pages 47–52

CA Standards
MR 1.0
MR 2.0
MR 3.0

1. Describe and correct the error made in solving the following problem.

   *You are ordering pizza for a party. One pizza serves 8 people. You expect that there will be 35 people at the party. How many pizzas should you order?*

   $$\begin{array}{r} 4\text{ R}3 \\ 8\overline{)35} \\ \underline{32} \\ 3 \end{array}$$

   You need to order 4 pizzas.

2. Farmers typically do not plant the same crop in the same plot of soil season after season. For each upcoming season, the farmer will switch positions of crops from the previous season to grow healthier plants. This is called crop rotation. The tables below show the rotation of crops for three seasons. If you continue the pattern, how many seasons will it take for the crops to be in the positions they were in the first season?

| Season 1 | | |
|---|---|---|
| Beans | Potatoes | Lettuce |
| Cabbage | Spinach | Carrots |

| Season 2 | | |
|---|---|---|
| Cabbage | Beans | Potatoes |
| Spinach | Carrots | Lettuce |

| Season 3 | | |
|---|---|---|
| Spinach | Cabbage | Beans |
| Carrots | Lettuce | Potatoes |

3. You have $100 to spend on a new outfit. You spend $25 on shoes and you still need pants and a shirt. You find 3 pants and 2 shirts that you like. The prices for the items are shown in the table. Which combinations of pants and a shirt could you buy with the money you have left?

| Item | Price |
|---|---|
| Tan pants | $48 |
| Navy pants | $34 |
| Black pants | $42 |
| Striped shirt | $38 |
| Solid shirt | $32 |

# Practice *continued*
For use with pages 47–52

**4.** A computer screen is divided into little squares called pixels. The number
of pixels on the screen is called the monitor resolution. A common
monitor resolution is $640 \times 480$, which means that there are 640 pixels
along the length of the screen and 480 pixels along the width of the
screen. If a computer program divides the screen into equal size
squares, what would be the length of the side in pixels of the largest
possible square?

**5.** A pizza shop offers five different toppings (pepperoni (R), onions (O),
peppers (P), sausage (S), and mushrooms (M)) for its pizzas. How many
different pizzas can be created using three different toppings? What are
the combinations of the toppings?

# Practice
For use with pages 69–73

**Complete the statement.**

**1.** $\dfrac{a}{c} + \dfrac{b}{c} = \dfrac{? + ?}{c}$

**2.** $\dfrac{?}{c} - \dfrac{?}{c} = \dfrac{a - b}{c}$

**Find the sum or difference. Simplify if possible.**

**3.** $\dfrac{1}{5} + \dfrac{2}{5}$

**4.** $\dfrac{8}{9} - \dfrac{3}{9}$

**5.** $\dfrac{3}{7} + \dfrac{3}{7}$

**6.** $\dfrac{10}{13} - \dfrac{3}{13}$

**7.** $\dfrac{5}{18} - \dfrac{2}{18}$

**8.** $\dfrac{6}{15} + \dfrac{3}{15}$

**9.** $\dfrac{2}{6} + \dfrac{3}{6}$

**10.** $\dfrac{17}{21} - \dfrac{5}{21}$

**11.** $\dfrac{19}{20} - \dfrac{3}{20}$

**12.** $\dfrac{11}{25} + \dfrac{7}{25}$

**13.** $\dfrac{8}{16} - \dfrac{2}{16}$

**14.** $\dfrac{25}{52} + \dfrac{1}{52}$

**In Exercises 15–17, use the following information. Three friends
decide to purchse a CD together as a birthday gift. Ashleigh
paid $\dfrac{3}{8}$, Jacob paid $\dfrac{1}{8}$, and Matthew paid $\dfrac{4}{8}$ of the price of the CD.**

**15.** What portion of the price did Matthew and Jacob pay?

**16.** What portion of the price did Ashleigh and Matthew pay?

**17.** How much greater was Matthew's portion than Jacob's?

# Practice *continued*
For use with pages 69–73

**Evaluate the expression for the given value of the variable.**

**18.** $x + \dfrac{2}{5}$, when $x = \dfrac{2}{5}$

**19.** $w - \dfrac{3}{11}$, when $w = \dfrac{7}{11}$

**20.** $\dfrac{8}{13} - m$, when $m = \dfrac{2}{13}$

**21.** $\dfrac{5}{9} + x$, when $x = \dfrac{2}{9}$

**22.** $w + \dfrac{3}{4}$, when $w = \dfrac{1}{4}$

**23.** $\dfrac{7}{8} - m$, when $m = \dfrac{5}{8}$.

**24.** You completed $\dfrac{5}{12}$ of your homework yesterday and $\dfrac{2}{12}$ of it today.

How much of your homework is complete?

Name _____  Date _____

**Find the sum or difference. Simplify if possible.**

**1.** $\dfrac{2}{3} + \dfrac{5}{6}$

**2.** $\dfrac{5}{7} - \dfrac{7}{14}$

**3.** $\dfrac{1}{2} - \dfrac{3}{8}$

**4.** $\dfrac{3}{8} + \dfrac{1}{4}$

**5.** $\dfrac{4}{5} - \dfrac{8}{15}$

**6.** $\dfrac{5}{12} + \dfrac{2}{5}$

**7.** $\dfrac{5}{6} - \dfrac{3}{4}$

**8.** $\dfrac{3}{7} + \dfrac{6}{8}$

**9.** $\dfrac{4}{9} + \dfrac{3}{4}$

**10.** $\dfrac{7}{11} - \dfrac{1}{3}$

**11.** $\dfrac{2}{5} + \dfrac{5}{6}$

**12.** $\dfrac{8}{9} - \dfrac{5}{7}$

**Evaluate the expression** $x = \dfrac{3}{4}$ **and** $y = \dfrac{5}{7}$.

**13.** $x + \dfrac{5}{12}$

**14.** $y + \dfrac{1}{2}$

**15.** $\dfrac{4}{5} - x$

**16.** $y - \dfrac{3}{8}$

**17.** $x + y$

**18.** $x - y$

**Find the perimeter of the figure.**

**19.**
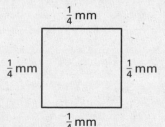

**20.**
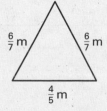

**21.**
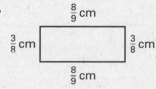

**LESSON 2.2** | **Practice** *continued*
For use with pages 74–80

22. You take a container of fruit juice to drink at practice. You get thirsty and drink $\frac{2}{9}$ of the juice before practice. What fraction of the original amount is left to drink at practice?

23. A farmer has three hay fields. The area of one field is $\frac{7}{8}$ acre. The area of another field is $\frac{5}{6}$ acre. The area of the third field is $\frac{11}{12}$ acre. What is the total area of the three fields?

24. Maria has $5\frac{6}{7}$ square yards of fabric. She uses $2\frac{2}{3}$ square yards of fabric to make a dress. Does she have enough fabric left over to make a shawl that takes $2\frac{1}{4}$ square yards of fabric?

*Lesson 2.2*

**LESSON 2.3** **Practice**
For use with pages 81–85

**Find the sum or difference. Write the answer in simplest form.**

**1.** $3\frac{2}{7} + 4\frac{5}{7}$

**2.** $5\frac{7}{12} - 3\frac{5}{12}$

**3.** $2\frac{3}{8} + 1\frac{7}{8}$

**4.** $8\frac{14}{15} - 5\frac{8}{15}$

**5.** $1\frac{2}{5} + 6\frac{8}{15}$

**6.** $5\frac{7}{9} - 3\frac{5}{18}$

**7.** $4\frac{5}{6} + 7\frac{7}{24}$

**8.** $10\frac{17}{21} - 4\frac{2}{3}$

**9.** $5\frac{3}{7} + 4\frac{1}{2}$

**10.** $8\frac{1}{4} - 3\frac{1}{3}$

**11.** $3\frac{5}{12} + 7\frac{2}{15}$

**12.** $5\frac{1}{9} - 2\frac{5}{6}$

**13.** Describe and correct the error in finding the difference $8\frac{1}{6} - 4\frac{2}{3}$.

$$8\frac{1}{6} - 4\frac{2}{3} = 8\frac{1}{6} - 4\frac{4}{6} = 7\frac{9}{6} - 4\frac{4}{6} = 3\frac{5}{6}$$

**Evaluate the expression when $x = 4\frac{3}{8}$ and $y = 7\frac{5}{6}$.**

**14.** $5\frac{2}{3} + x$

**15.** $y - 4\frac{2}{3}$

**16.** $x + y$

**LESSON 2.3**  **Practice** *continued*
For use with pages 81–85

**Complete the statement using $<$, $>$, or $=$.**

**17.** $8\frac{2}{3} - 7\frac{1}{4}$ __?__ 1

**18.** $4\frac{1}{6} + 5\frac{3}{8}$ __?__ 10

**19.** $7\frac{1}{4} + 3\frac{3}{7}$ __?__ 11

**Evaluate the expression. Write the answer in simplest form.**

**20.** $3\frac{1}{2} + 6\frac{2}{3} + 4\frac{7}{12}$

**21.** $8\frac{9}{16} + 5\frac{3}{8} - 3\frac{1}{4}$

**22.** $12\frac{5}{24} + 7\frac{1}{8} - 8\frac{3}{4}$

**23.** A rye bread recipe calls for $1\frac{7}{8}$ cups bread flour and $1\frac{1}{2}$ cups rye flour. How many cups of flour do you need altogether?

**24.** The largest species of praying mantis grows to be about 6 inches long. The smallest species of praying mantis grows to be $\frac{2}{5}$ inches long. How much longer is the largest species than the smallest species?

Name _____ Date _____

**Find the product. Write the answer in simplest form.**

**1.** $\dfrac{1}{8} \times \dfrac{3}{7}$

**2.** $\dfrac{4}{5} \times \dfrac{10}{11}$

**3.** $\dfrac{6}{7} \times \dfrac{15}{16}$

**4.** $\dfrac{7}{10} \times \dfrac{25}{28}$

**5.** $12 \times \dfrac{3}{4}$

**6.** $\dfrac{5}{6} \times 24$

**7.** $2\dfrac{2}{3} \times 1\dfrac{4}{5}$

**8.** $8\dfrac{1}{2} \times 1\dfrac{7}{9}$

**9.** $5\dfrac{3}{4} \times 10\dfrac{2}{3}$

**10.** $3 \times 4\dfrac{4}{7}$

**11.** $6 \times 6\dfrac{3}{5}$

**12.** $4\dfrac{1}{3} \times \dfrac{2}{3}$

**13.** Find the area of the rectangle.

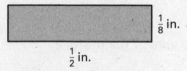

$\frac{1}{8}$ in.

$\frac{1}{2}$ in.

**14.** Which two products have the same value?

**A.** $1\dfrac{1}{3} \times \dfrac{2}{5}$

**B.** $1\dfrac{2}{3} \times \dfrac{3}{5}$

**C.** $1\dfrac{1}{4} \times 1\dfrac{1}{2}$

**D.** $\dfrac{4}{5} \times \dfrac{2}{3}$

**LESSON 2.4** **Practice** *continued*
For use with pages 87–92

**15.** Choose the product that best estimates $5\frac{2}{3} \times 4\frac{1}{5}$.

   **A.** $5 \times 4$          **B.** $6 \times 4$          **C.** $6 \times 5$          **D.** $5 \times 5$

**Estimate the product. *Explain* your method.**

**16.** $\frac{7}{8} \times 5\frac{1}{6}$          **17.** $2\frac{1}{3} \times 5\frac{3}{5}$          **18.** $4\frac{1}{3} \times 5\frac{3}{5}$

**19.** A deer mouse is $7\frac{1}{4}$ inches long, including its tail. If the tail is one-half its total body length, how long is the tail?

**20.** A mirror is $13\frac{1}{2}$ inches wide and $21\frac{1}{4}$ inches long. What is the area of the mirror?

Name _____  Date _____

**LESSON 2.5** **Practice**
For use with pages 94–100

CA Standards
NS 2.1

**Write the reciprocal of the number.**

1. $\frac{1}{5}$

2. $2$

3. $1\frac{4}{5}$

4. $3\frac{6}{11}$

5. Which expression is the related multiplication expression for $\frac{4}{5} \div \frac{2}{9}$?

A. $\frac{4}{5} \times \frac{2}{9}$

B. $\frac{4}{5} \times \frac{9}{2}$

C. $\frac{5}{4} \times \frac{2}{9}$

D. $\frac{5}{4} \times \frac{9}{2}$

**Find the quotient. Then check your answer.**

6. $\frac{2}{9} \div \frac{1}{3}$

7. $\frac{3}{4} \div \frac{5}{8}$

8. $\frac{4}{9} \div \frac{9}{20}$

9. $\frac{2}{3} \div \frac{5}{18}$

10. $\frac{9}{14} \div 7$

11. $9 \div 4\frac{2}{3}$

12. $6\frac{3}{4} \div 5\frac{1}{2}$

13. $3\frac{2}{5} \div 8$

14. $4\frac{1}{6} \div 3\frac{2}{5}$

15. Describe and correct the error in finding the quotient $\frac{4}{5} \div 3\frac{2}{3}$.

$$\frac{4}{5} \div 3\frac{2}{3} = \frac{4}{5} \div \frac{11}{3} = \frac{5}{4} \times \frac{11}{3} = 4\frac{7}{12}$$

Name _____   Date _____

**Practice** *continued*
For use with pages 94–100

**Evaluate the expression when** $x = \frac{3}{5}$ **and** $y = 8$.

**16.** $x \div y$          **17.** $y \div x$          **18.** $1\frac{1}{3} \div x$

**Complete the statement using** $<, >,$ **or** $=$.

**19.** $\frac{1}{2} \div \frac{2}{5}$ __?__ $1$      **20.** $\frac{7}{8} \div \frac{1}{9}$ __?__ $1$      **21.** $1\frac{2}{5} \div 2\frac{1}{4}$ __?__ $1$

**22.** You are cutting pieces of wire that are each $14\frac{1}{4}$ inches long for an art project. If you have a spool with 114 inches of wire, how many pieces of wire can you cut from the spool?

**23.** The largest and smallest sea urchins on record measured about $1\frac{1}{4}$ feet and $\frac{1}{50}$ foot long, respectively. How many times larger is the largest sea urchin?

# LESSON 2.6 Practice
For use with pages 101–106

**Find the sum or difference. Check the reasonableness of your answer.**

**1.** $12.5 + 3.7$

**2.** $54.6 + 2.765$

**3.** $35.4 - 8.9$

**4.** $142.6 - 37.42$

**5.** $0.54 + 13.77$

**6.** $94.32 + 14.829$

**7.** $67.312 - 5.47$

**8.** $20.27 - 5.79$

**9.** $8.215 + 104.56$

**Fill in the missing digit.**

**10.**
$$\begin{array}{r} 8.76 \\ + 2.9? \\ \hline 11.71 \end{array}$$

**11.**
$$\begin{array}{r} 37.25 \\ + 84.?6 \\ \hline 121.61 \end{array}$$

**12.**
$$\begin{array}{r} 24.75 \\ - 1?.48 \\ \hline 8.27 \end{array}$$

**Evaluate the expression when $x = 39.6$ and $y = 14.65$.**

**13.** $12.7 + y$

**14.** $y - 5.9$

**15.** $x + y$

**16.** $x - y$

**17.** $y - 2.73$

**18.** $27 - y$

**Estimate the sum or difference using front-end estimation.**

**19.** $2.84 + 3.21$

**20.** $12.62 + 9.34$

# Practice continued
For use with pages 101–106

**21.** $10.85 - 5.19$         **22.** $2.77 + 4 + 13.25$

**23.** $6.04 + 18.85 + 10.25$       **24.** $8.88 - 3.2$

**Evaluate the expression.**

**25.** $347.4 + 2.29 + 14$

**26.** $79 - 2.304 - 16.7$

**27.** $65.84 + 7.013 + 14.6$

**28.** A quarter horse has a top running speed of 47.5 miles per hour and a greyhound has a top running speed of 39.35 miles per hour. How much faster than the greyhound can the quarter horse run?

**29.** During the 1880s, the average temperature of Earth was 56.65 degrees Fahrenheit. During the 1980s, the average temperature of Earth was 57.36 degrees Fahrenheit. How much warmer was Earth's average temperature in the 1980s than in the 1880s?

**30.** You are mailing a 4-pound package, an 8-pound package, and a 9-pound package to another city. It will cost $4.86 to mail the 4-pound package, $5.98 to mail the 8-pound package, and $6.11 to mail the 9-pound package. Use front-end estimation to estimate how much it will cost you to mail all three packages.

**LESSON 2.7** **Practice**
For use with pages 107–113

**Find the product. Then check that your answer is reasonable.**

**1.** $4.1 \times 3.5$      **2.** $7.6 \times 2.3$      **3.** $0.4 \times 0.04$

**4.** $0.08 \times 7$      **5.** $0.14 \times 0.85$      **6.** $2.01 \times 3.14$

**7.** $6.3 \times 4.005$      **8.** $0.86 \times 5.041$      **9.** $0.004 \times 0.057$

**Estimate the product.**

**10.** $7.41 \times 82.3$      **11.** $0.46 \times 3.1$      **12.** $0.15 \times 6.72$

**Find the quotient. Round your answer to the nearest hundredth if necessary.**

**13.** $300.3 \div 42$      **14.** $12 \div 2.4$      **15.** $0.156 \div 1.2$

**16.** $1.89 \div 3.6$      **17.** $4.064 \div 2.54$      **18.** $3.4 \div 1.36$

**19.** $0.347 \div 8$      **20.** $25 \div 3.7$      **21.** $11.02 \div 4.25$

**Use compatible numbers to estimate the quotient.**

**22.** $120.56 \div 2.98$      **23.** $1404.59 \div 73.6$      **24.** $378.5 \div 61.8$

Lesson 2.7

**LESSON 2.7** **Practice** *continued*
For use with pages 107–113

**Evaluate the expression when $a = 4.23$ and $b = 6.04$.**

**25.** $3.5a$          **26.** $27.5b$          **27.** $ab$

**28.** $b \div 0.16$          **29.** $a \div 1.25$          **30.** $19.035 \div a$

**31.** A gallon of apple cider costs \$3.54. How much will it cost you to buy 4 gallons of apple cider?

**32.** In 2005, the average annual salary for a person living in Boulder, Colorado was about 1.103 times the average annual salary for a person living in the Seattle, Washington area. If the average annual salary in Seattle was \$41,661, what was the average annual salary in Boulder? Round your answer to the nearest dollar.

**33.** It costs you \$8.95 to buy five rolls of film at a store. How much does it cost for one roll of the film?

**34.** The area of Long Beach California is 50.4 square miles. In 2005, the population of Long Beach was 474,014. Find the population density of Long Beach in 2005 by dividing its population by its area. Round your answer to the nearest tenth.

**LESSON 3.1** **Practice**
For use with pages 129–133

**Write the integer that represents the situation. Then write the opposite of that integer.**

**1.** A $52 account withdrawal

**2.** Seventeen degrees below zero

**Draw a number line and graph the integer. Then give a real-life situation that the integer could represent.**

**3.** $-6$

**4.** 2

**5.** the opposite of 4

**Complete the statement using < or >.**

**6.** 27 _?_ $-72$

**7.** $-8$ _?_ $-15$

**8.** 62 _?_ 59

**9.** $-12$ _?_ 6

**10.** 35 _?_ $-35$

**11.** $-8$ _?_ 2

**Name two integer values of the variable that make the statement true.**

**12.** $0 < x$

**13.** $a < 32$

**14.** $-18 > y$

**Order the integers from least to greatest.**

**15.** $16, -5, 8, -23, 51, 0$

**16.** $-30, 20, 9, -12, 0, -10$

**17.** $89, -44, 15, -3, 9, -48$

**18.** $-130, 215, -501, 125, -42, 18$

**LESSON**
**3.1**

# Practice *continued*
For use with pages 129–133

**Lesson 3.1**

**Tell whether the statement is *true* or *false*. Explain your reasoning.**

**19.** $-8 < 7$

**20.** $-14 > -18$

**21.** $5 > -2$

**22.** $-5 > -1$

**23.** $0 > -12$

**24.** $-24 < -27$

**25.** The lowest temperature recorded in Indiana was 36 degrees below zero. The lowest temperature recorded in Arkansas was 29 degrees below zero. Which temperature was lower?

**26.** The table lists five countries and the number of hours each country's time is ahead of or behind Eastern Standard Time (EST). Use a number line to order the number of hours from least to greatest. Let positive integers represent the number of hours ahead of EST and let negative integers represent the number of hours behind EST.

| Country or Territory | Hours from EST |
|---|---|
| American Samoa | 6 hours behind |
| Costa Rica | 1 hour behind |
| Cuba | 0 hours ahead |
| French Polynesia | 5 hours behind |
| Germany | 6 hours ahead |

Name _____ Date _____

**Write the addition expression modeled on the number line. Then find the sum.**

1.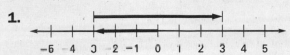

2.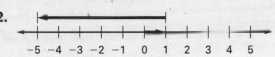

**Find the absolute value of the number.**

3. 25                4. $-13$                5. 0

**Find the sum.**

6. $14 + (-8)$          7. $-35 + 24$          8. $-5 + (-12)$

9. $-19 + 23$          10. $18 + (-31)$          11. $-8 + (-15)$

12. $13 + (-13)$          13. $-3 + 17 + (-4)$          14. $5 + (-11) + 14$

**Complete the statement using <, >, or =.**

15. $|-8|$ __?__ 5          16. $0$ __?__ $|-12|$          17. $|-6|$ __?__ $|6|$

18. $-7$ __?__ $|3|$          19. $|-4|$ __?__ $|-9|$          20. $13$ __?__ $|-13|$

Lesson 3.2

**LESSON
3.2** **Practice** *continued*
For use with pages 134–140

**Evaluate the expression when $a = 8$ and $b = -5$.**

**21.** $-17 + a$      **22.** $b + (-4)$      **23.** $3 + b$

**24.** Which addition expression has a sum of 11?

   **A.** $27 + (-15)$      **B.** $-8 + (-3)$      **C.** $-14 + 25$      **D.** $20 + (-31)$

**25.** In January, the normal high temperature in Bismarck, North Dakota, is 22 degrees warmer than its normal low temperature. If Bismarck's normal low temperature is $-2°F$ in January, what is its normal high temperature?

**26.** At the beginning of the week, you have $42 in your savings account. During the week, you deposit $25 and withdraw $36. How much money is in your account at the end of the week?

**27.** The lowest point in Europe is the Caspian Sea at an elevation of 92 feet below sea level. The highest point in Europe is Mount Elbrus, which is 18,602 feet above the Caspian Sea. What is the elevation of Mount Elbrus?

**LESSON 3.3**  **Practice**
For use with pages 141–147

CA Standards
NS 2.3

**Find the difference.**

**1.** $-16 - 7$  **2.** $14 - (-17)$  **3.** $11 - 28$

**4.** $30 - 12$  **5.** $5 - (-5)$  **6.** $-4 - (-34)$

**7.** $-63 - (-9)$  **8.** $-44 - 35$  **9.** $52 - (-79)$

**Evaluate the expression when $a = 5$ and $b = -14$.**

**10.** $b - 10$  **11.** $a - (-27)$  **12.** $12 - b$

**Copy and complete the statement using $<$, $>$, or $=$.**

**13.** $-3 - (-4)$ _?_ $5$  **14.** $4 - 8$ _?_ $16$  **15.** $-17 + 5$ _?_ $12$

**Tell whether the statement is *true* or *false*.**

**16.** The difference of a positive integer and a negative integer is always positive.

**17.** The difference of a negative integer and a negative integer is always negative.

**18.** The difference of a negative integer and a positive integer is sometimes positive.

Lesson 3.3

**LESSON 3.3** **Practice** *continued*
For use with pages 141–147

**19.** The highest point in California is Mount Whitney at 14,494 feet above sea level. The lowest point in California is Death Valley at 282 feet below sea level. What is the difference in the elevations?

**20.** A temperature expressed using kelvin units (K) can be converted to degrees Celsius (°C) by subtracting 273. Convert the boiling points of the gases given in the table from kelvins to degrees Celsius.

| Gas | Boiling Point |
|-----|---------------|
| Argon | 87 K |
| Helium | 4 K |
| Krypton | 120 K |
| Neon | 27 K |

**21.** The temperature at 6 P.M. was 8°F. Three hours later the temperature was −11°F. What was the change in temperature?

Lesson 3.3

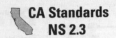CA Standards
NS 2.3

**LESSON
3.4**
# Practice
For use with pages 148–152

**Find the product.**

**1.** 4(15)

**2.** 8(−6)

**3.** −11(9)

**4.** −24(−3)

**5.** −14(5)

**6.** 25( 30)

**7.** −17(0)

**8.** −3(2)(5)

**9.** −2(−5)(4)

**10.** 150(−4)

**11.** −200(−75)

**12.** −8(0)(7)

**Complete the statement using <, >, or =.**

**13.** 17 • (−3) __?__ 25 • (−2)

**14.** −18 • (−2) __?__ 7 • 5

**15.** −24 • 2 __?__ 6 • (−8)

**Evaluate the expression when a = −4, b = −3, and c = −9.**

**16.** 3 • b

**17.** 9 • a

**18.** 5 • (−9) • c

**19.** −7 • (−4) • b

**20.** 0 • (−4) • a

**21.** 8 • c

Lesson 3.4

**LESSON**
**3.4**

# Practice *continued*
For use with pages 148–152

**Copy and complete the statement using mental math.**

**22.** $-4 \cdot \underline{\ ?\ } = 32$     **23.** $3 \cdot \underline{\ ?\ } = -36$     **24.** $-2 \cdot \underline{\ ?\ } = -28$

**25.** A beluga whale is diving downward at a speed of 2 meters per second. What integer represents the whale's change in position after 45 seconds?

**26.** The record low temperature in Louisiana is $-16°F$. The record low temperature in Maine is three times lower than the record low in Louisiana. What is the record low temperature in Maine?

**27.** A sump pump can be used to pump large amounts of water out of basements that have been flooded. One sump pump model removes water from a basement at a rate of 45 gallons per minute. Write and simplify an expression to represent the change in the amount of water in the basement after 5 minutes.

*Lesson 3.4*

**LESSON 3.5** **Practice**
For use with pages 154–158

**Find the quotient.**

**1.** $-66 \div 11$

**2.** $72 \div (-3)$

**3.** $-96 \div (-12)$

**4.** $80 \div (-20)$

**5.** $-125 \div (-5)$

**6.** $-124 \div 31$

**7.** $0 \div (-23)$

**8.** $-325 \div 13$

**9.** $-147 \div (-7)$

**Find the mean of the integers.**

**10.** $-5, 0, 2, 3$

**11.** $-8, -6, 5, 5$

**12.** $-4, -3, 1, 3, 8$

**13.** $-6, -5, 5, 7, 9$

**14.** $9, -12, 19, -9$

**15.** $5, 12, -12, -5, 0$

**16.** Find the quotient of negative 150 and positive 10.

**17.** Find the quotient of positive 75 and negative 25.

**18.** Find the quotient of negative 84 and negative 6.

Name _____     Date _____

**Evaluate the expression when $m = 25$ and $n = -6$.**

**19.** $m \div (-5)$      **20.** $-54 \div n$      **21.** $-225 \div m$

**22.** $0 \div n$      **23.** $n \div 3$      **24.** $78 \div n$

**Complete the statement using $<$, $>$, or $=$.**

**25.** $15 \div (-3)$ __?__ $15 \div 3$      **26.** $76 \div (-19)$ __?__ $-76 \div 19$

**27.** $24 \div 8$ __?__ $-24 \div 8$      **28.** $0 \div 5$ __?__ $0 \div 9$

**29.** $42 \div (-6) \div (-1)$ __?__ $7$      **30.** $-30 \div (-5) \div (-1)$ __?__ $6$

**31.** The gains and losses in the worth of a share of stock over a 5-day period are $6, $2, $-\$1$, $-\$3$, and $1. Find the mean change in worth of the stock over the 5-day period.

**32.** The low temperatures for a town during a week in January are shown in the table. Find the mean of the temperatures.

| Day | Monday | Tuesday | Wednesday | Thursday | Friday | Saturday | Sunday |
|---|---|---|---|---|---|---|---|
| **Temperature** | $-15°F$ | $-9°F$ | $2°F$ | $0°F$ | $-3°F$ | $-5°F$ | $2°F$ |

## LESSON 3.6 Practice

For use with pages 160–166

CA Standards
AF 1.4
NS 2.3

**Evaluate the expression.**

**1.** $10 + 6 \cdot 8$

**2.** $35 - 20 \div 5$

**3.** $18(11 - 6)$

**4.** $28 \div (16 - 9)$

**5.** $\dfrac{14 + 10}{7 - 4}$

**6.** $33 \div (3^2 + 2)$

**7.** $5(7 + 5)^2$

**8.** $(5 - 3)^3 + 12 \div 4$

**9.** $11(8 + 3^2) - 15$

**10.** $3 \cdot 4 \cdot 12 - 7$

**11.** $3 \cdot 4^2 + 12$

**12.** $\dfrac{5 \cdot 12}{4}$

**13.** $4 \cdot 9^2 - 12$

**14.** $\dfrac{12 - 9}{3}$

**15.** $(12 - 4)^2 + 14$

**16.** $\dfrac{4 + 12}{9 - 5}$

**17.** $(4^2 - 12)(9 + 4)$

**18.** $36 \div 9 - 4$

| LESSON | **Practice** *continued* |
|--------|--------------------------|
| **3.6** | For use with pages 160–166 |

**Match the given expression with the expression that has the same value.**

**19.** $36 - 5^2 + 7$

**A.** $2^2 \cdot 8 - 10$

**20.** $27 - 2 \cdot 4 + 3$

**B.** $(4^2 + 38) \div 3$

**21.** $12(8 - 3)$

**C.** $(5 + 3)^2 - 4$

**22.** Your local phone company offers DSL service for connecting to the Internet. There is a one-time $100 hookup fee and monthly charges are $40 for the service. Write and evaluate an expression to find the cost of getting DSL service for the first year.

**23.** At the beginning of the workday, a cashier will start out with money in his or her cash register so that change can be made. A cash register contains 50 one-dollar bills, 30 five-dollar bills, and 8 ten-dollar bills. Write and evaluate an expression that will give you the total amount of money in the cash register.

**LESSON 3.7** **Practice**
For use with pages 167–172

**Show that the number is rational by writing it in $\frac{a}{b}$ form. Then give the multiplicative inverse and the additive inverse of the number.**

**1.** $-\dfrac{4}{7}$

**2.** $8\dfrac{2}{5}$

**3.** $0.6$

**4.** $15$

**5.** $-1\dfrac{1}{2}$

**6.** $-0.25$

**Use a number line to order the rational numbers from least to greatest.**

**7.** $-5.2,\ -4,\ -\dfrac{13}{3},\ -4\dfrac{1}{2},\ -5$

**8.** $6,\ -5\dfrac{1}{2},\ 0,\ -\dfrac{8}{3},\ -0.79$

**9.** $\dfrac{4}{5},\ -\dfrac{6}{7},\ 0.05,\ 1,\ -0.3$

**Evaluate the expression. Justify each step you take.**

**10.** $53 + 22 + 67$

**11.** $\dfrac{1}{4} + \dfrac{3}{7} + \left(-\dfrac{1}{4}\right)$

**12.** $12 \cdot \dfrac{2}{5} \cdot \dfrac{1}{12}$

**13.** $-4.8 + [3 + (-1.2)]$

**14.** $[6 \cdot (-3)] \cdot 15$

**15.** $4 \cdot 11 \cdot 25$

**LESSON
3.7** | **Practice** *continued*
For use with pages 167–172

**Complete the statement using $<$, $>$, or $=$.**

**16.** $-\dfrac{2}{3} + \dfrac{5}{6} + \dfrac{2}{3}$ __?__ 1    **17.** $\dfrac{7}{8} \cdot \dfrac{6}{1} \cdot \dfrac{8}{7}$ __?__ 6    **18.** $(-18.4 + 23) + (-4.6)$ __?__ 0

**19.** The recorded rainfall (in inches) for a town for the first three months of the year was 1.36, 0.87, and 2.04. Write and simplify an expression to find the total amount of rainfall for the three months. Justify each step you take.

**20.** A music store sells drumsticks for $10 per pair. The store buys the drumsticks in boxes that contain 12 pairs of sticks per box. The expression $\dfrac{1}{12} \cdot 10 \cdot 12$ gives the amount of money the store will earn from selling $\dfrac{1}{12}$ of a box of drumsticks. Find the amount of money earned from selling the drumsticks. Justify each step you take.

Lesson 3.7

**LESSON 3.8** **Practice**
For use with pages 173–178

CA Standards
AF 1.3

**1.** Use the distributive property to write an equation for the model.

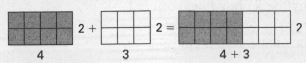

$$2 + \quad 2 = \quad ?$$

$$4 \qquad 3 \qquad 4 + 3$$

**Use the distributive property to write an equivalent expression.
Check your answer.**

**2.** $7(6 + 4)$

**3.** $8(8 + 5)$

**4.** $9(3) + 9(5)$

**5.** $6(100 - 8)$

**6.** $5\left(\dfrac{13}{16}\right) - 5\left(\dfrac{5}{16}\right)$

**7.** $12\left(\dfrac{2}{3}\right) + 12\left(\dfrac{1}{3}\right)$

**Use the distributive property to evaluate the expression.**

**8.** $2(6.5) + 2(3.5)$

**9.** $12(3.8) + 12(1.2)$

**10.** $7(15.8) + 7(4.2)$

**11.** $15\left(\dfrac{3}{4}\right) + 15\left(\dfrac{1}{4}\right)$

**12.** $19\left(\dfrac{2}{5}\right) - 19\left(-\dfrac{3}{5}\right)$

**13.** $6(10.7)$

**Evaluate the expression and justify your steps.**

**14.** $13(12) + 13(-11) - 1$

**15.** $\dfrac{7}{4}\left(\dfrac{3}{7}\right) + \dfrac{7}{4}\left(\dfrac{1}{7}\right) + (-1)$

**Use the distributive property to find the missing number or
variable.**

**16.** $b \cdot 15 + b \cdot 9 = b(15 + \underline{\ ?\ })$

**17.** $14 \cdot 6 + 14 \cdot \underline{\ ?\ } = 14(6 + y)$

Lesson 3.8

**LESSON
3.8**

# Practice *continued*
For use with pages 173–178

18. You and three friends are taking a trip to the zoo. The zoo charges
$12 for admission and you all decide to buy the $5 box lunch offered
by the zoo. Use the distributive property to write two equivalent
expressions to represent the total cost of the visit for your entire
group. Then find the total cost for the group.

19. You buy five CDs at a sale for $5.95 each. Write an expression for
the total cost of the CDs. Then use the distributive property and
mental math to evaluate the expression.

20. You are carpeting two rooms in your home. One room is 7 feet long
and 6 feet wide, and the other is 8 feet long and 6 feet wide. Use the
distributive property to write two equivalent expressions to represent
the total area of the two rooms. Then find the total area of the two
rooms.

Lesson 3.8

Name _____     Date _____

# Practice
For use with pages 197–201

**Evaluate the expression for the given values of the variables.**

**1.** $4c - 8d$ when $c = -9$ and $d = -3$

**2.** $\frac{a}{b}$ when $a = 6.8$ and $b = 27.2$

**3.** $r^2 + \frac{8}{9}s - 4t$ when $r = -3$, $s = 63$, and $t = 7.5$

**4.** $\frac{5m - n}{16 - 5p}$ when $m = 4.2$, $n = -4$, and $p = \frac{7}{10}$

**5.** You earn $10 for mowing a lawn and your part-time summer job pays $7.25 per hour. To find the amount of money you earn this week, you can evaluate the expression $7.25h + 10$, where $h$ is the number of hours you worked during the week. If you work 15 hours this week, how much money do you earn for the week?

**6.** To find the number of calories from protein in a serving of food, you can evaluate the expression $4g$, where $g$ is the number of grams of protein in a serving. If a serving of nuts contains 12.5 grams of protein, how many calories from protein are in the serving?

**Evaluate the expression when $a = -3$, $b = 8.3$, $m = \frac{2}{5}$, and $q = 6.6$.**

**7.** $b + q$

**8.** $q - 5m$

**9.** $10m - 4a$

**10.** $bq + 24.12$

**11.** $\frac{a + 27}{14.3 - b}$

**12.** $30m - a^2 + q$

Lesson 4.1

**13.** The Pennsylvania Turnpike is a 528-mile long roadway that spans the entire state. To find how long it will take you to drive across the state on the turnpike, you can evaluate the expression $\frac{L}{r}$, where $L$ is the length of the Pennsylvania Turnpike and $r$ is your driving speed. If you maintain a driving speed of 66 miles per hour, how many hours will it take you to drive across the state?

**14.** Which two expressions are the same?

**A.** $\dfrac{a}{b}$  **B.** $a - b$

**C.** $a \div b$  **D.** $\dfrac{b}{a}$

**LESSON 4.2** **Practice**
For use with pages 202–206

**Write the verbal phrase as an algebraic expression. Let $n$ represent the number.**

**1.** A number added to 10.4

**2.** $-14$ decreased by a number

**3.** $\frac{1}{4}$ times a number

**4.** A number increased by $-13$

**Write the phrase as an algebraic expression.**

**5.** 11 decreased by the quotient of $u$ and $v$

**6.** Twice $a$ subtracted from 1

**7.** $p$ squared divided by the sum of $n$ and $r$

**8.** $b$ times the difference of $\frac{1}{8}$ and $c$

**9.** $g$ plus the product of $h$ to the fourth power and $j$

**10.** The sum of 6.7 and $a$ divided by the difference of $b$ and 3.9

**Write a verbal phrase for the algebraic expression.**

**11.** $x + 12y$

**12.** $9.8 - ab$

**13.** $\frac{m}{5} + \frac{n}{4}$

**14.** $a(b^2 + c)$

**15.** $\frac{s+t}{u}$

**16.** $5.2(x + y + z)$

**LESSON 4.2** **Practice** *continued*
For use with pages 202–206

**Write the real-world phrase as an algebraic expression. Be sure to identify what the variable represents.**

**17.** 1.6 miles more than yesterday's run

**18.** Two times your previous high score

**19.** One-third of the recipe

**20.** 3 inches shorter than your other dog

**21.** Yosemite National Park has many natural waterfalls within its boundaries, including Horsetail Fall and Yosemite Falls. Yosemite Falls is 1425 feet taller than Horsetail Fall. Write an algebraic expression to represent the height of Yosemite Falls. If Horsetail Fall is 1000 feet tall, what is the height of Yosemite Falls?

**22.** The population of Cape Coral, Florida increased by 38 thousand people from 2000 to 2005. Write an algebraic expression to represent the population in 2000. If the population of Cape Coral was 140 thousand people in 2005, what was the population in 2000?

**23.** In 2006, the cost of mailing a letter was 19.5 times the cost of mailing a letter in 1885. Write an algebraic expression to represent the cost of mailing a letter in 1885. If it cost $.39 to mail a letter in 2006, what was the cost of mailing a letter in 1885?

## LESSON 4.3 Practice
For use with pages 207–210

**Tell whether the statement is *true* or *false*.**

1. The coefficients of the expression $8 - 5x - 4 + 3x$ are 5 and 3.

2. The constants of the expression $-4 + 11x + 9 - 8x$ are $-4$ and 9.

3. In the expression $3x - 9 + 3 - 10x$, $3x$ and 3 are like terms.

4. The expressions $15x - 9 - 4x + 2$ and $11x - 7$ are equivalent.

**Identify the coefficients, like terms, and constant terms of the expression.**

5. $8.4x + 9.3 - 3.7x$

6. $17 - 2a + 5a - 1$

7. $\frac{3}{7}m - \frac{2}{7} + \frac{5}{6}m$

8. $10.2 + 15.6r - 2.9r + 28.3$

**Match the expression with an equivalent expression.**

9. $5x - 4 - 3x + 9$

A. $2x - 3$

10. $5(x - 3) - 3x + 7$

B. $2x + 5$

11. $-5x + 6 + 7x - 9$

C. $2x - 8$

**Simplify the expression.**

**12.** $3(5 + 4b) - 2$

**13.** $6(3 - 2z) + 11z - 4$

**14.** $7(1.8n - 4) + 13 - 5.2n$

**15.** $2\left(\dfrac{1}{4}x + 6 + \dfrac{3}{16}x\right) + 8$

**16.** $-6(8 + 4r) - 12r - 3 + 5r$

**17.** $15.7 + 12(1.3a + 7) - 4.8a$

**18.** A nut mixture contains peanuts, walnuts, and cashews. In the mixture, the amount of peanuts is 3.5 times the amount of cashews, and the amount of walnuts is 4.25 times the amount of cashews. Let $x$ represent the amount of cashews. Write and simplify an expression for the total amount of nuts in the mixture.

**19.** Jacksonville, Florida, received $r$ inches of rain in September. In October, Jacksonville received $\dfrac{4}{9}$ as much rain as in September. Write and simplify an expression to represent the total amount of rainfall in Jacksonville through September and October.

**20.** A basketball player scored 8 points total during the first and second quarters of a game. During the third quarter, she scored one-third as many points as she did in the fourth quarter. Let $x$ represent the number of points the player scored in the fourth quarter. Write and simplify an expression to represent the total number of points the player scored during the entire game.

Name _____ Date _____

**LESSON 4.4**

# Practice
For use with pages 211–217

CA Standards
AF 3.1
AF 3.2

**Write and simplify an expression for the perimeter of the figure.**

1.

$2p$

$15p$

2.

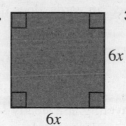

$6x$

$6x$

3.

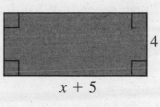

4

$x + 5$

**Write and simplify expressions for the perimeter and area of a rectangle with the given dimensions.**

4. $\ell = 5.2y, \, w = y - 1$

5. $\ell = c, \, w = 5c + 1$

6. $\ell = m + 3, \, w = 3m$

**Find the distance for the given rate and time.**

7. $r = 18$ mi/min, $t = 3$ min

8. $r = 12$ in./sec, $t = 7$ sec

9. $r = 55$ ft/h, $t = 6$ h

10. $r = 8.5$ cm/sec, $t = 11$ sec

11. $r = 17$ yd/min, $t = (x - 4)$ min

12. $r = 5x$ km/h, $t = 2.5$ h

**13.** A cheetah can run at a speed of 70 miles per hour (or 34.2 yards per second). What distance, in yards, does the cheetah travel in 5.5 seconds?

**14.** Claire is driving a car traveling at a steady speed of 63 miles per hour. She drives for 3 hours. How far does she drive?

**Convert the temperature from degrees Fahrenheit to degrees Celsius or from degrees Celsius to degrees Fahrenheit.**

**15.** 45°C          **16.** 150°C          **17.** 59°F

**18.** The melting point of the metal gallium is 86°F. What is this temperature in degrees Celsius?

**19.** The melting point of sulfur is 120°C. What is this temperature in degrees Fahrenheit?

**LESSON 4.5** **Practice**
For use with pages 219–224

CA Standards
AF 1.1

## Tell whether the number is a solution of the equation.

**1.** $7x = 42; 6$

**2.** $7 + a = 19; 12$

**3.** $z \div 4 = 6; 2$

**4.** $b - 16 = 28; 34$

**5.** $n + 8 = 21; 13$

**6.** $33 - y = 18; 25$

## Match the equation with the corresponding question. Then solve.

**7.** $6x = 48$

**8.** $x \div 6 = 8$

**9.** $6 + x = 48$

**10.** $\frac{48}{x} = 6$

**A.** 6 plus what number equals 48?

**B.** What number divided by 6 equals 8?

**C.** 6 times what number equals 48?

**D.** 48 divided by what number equals 6?

## Solve the equation using mental math.

**11.** $b + 15 = 23$

**12.** $25 - x = 16$

**13.** $\frac{40}{a} = 8$

**14.** $7m = 56$

**15.** $\frac{y}{4} = 10$

**16.** $p - 12 = 7$

## Use the formula for distance to find the unknown time.

**17.** $d = 100$ miles, $r = 20$ miles per hour, $t = \underline{\quad ? \quad}$

**18.** $d = 360$ kilometers, $r = 40$ kilometers per hour, $t = \underline{\quad ? \quad}$

Name _____    Date _____

# Practice continued
For use with pages 219–224

**19.** $d = 420$ miles, $r = 60$ miles per hour, $t =$ ___?___

**20.** The slowest flying bird in the world flies at a speed of 5 miles per hour. How long does it take for the bird to fly 15 miles?

**21.** Telescopes are described by their f/number. The f/number is given by the equation $f = F \div D$, where $f$ is the f/number, $F$ is the focal length of the telescope, and $D$ is the width of the telescope lens. Use the f/number equation to find the focal length (in inches) of a telescope with a 10-inch wide lens and an f/number of 9.

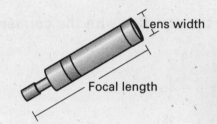

Lens width

Focal length

**22.** Two scales used for measuring temperature are the Kelvin scale and the Celsius scale. A temperature on the Kelvin scale is about 273 more than the temperature in degrees Celsius. Solve the equation $300 = C + 273$ to find the temperature in degrees Celsius that is the same as 300 on the Kelvin scale.

**LESSON 4.6**  **Practice**
For use with pages 225–231

**Tell whether the number is a solution of the equation.**

**1.** $x + 15 = 20; 5$

**2.** $a - 12 = 13; 1$

**3.** $7 + m = -31; 24$

**Solve the equation. Graph and check your solution.**

**4.** $y + 6 = 15$

**5.** $n + 23 = -14$

**6.** $18 = r + 7$

**7.** $a - 12 = 28$

**8.** $z - 24 = -9$

**9.** $20 = s - 35$

**10.** $3.6 + m = 12.5$

**11.** $c - 2.1 = 6.7$

**12.** $4.2 + x - 1.4 = 7.5$

**13.** $t - \dfrac{1}{5} = \dfrac{3}{10}$

**14.** $\dfrac{6}{7} = a + \dfrac{2}{7}$

**15.** $\dfrac{2}{3} + x - \dfrac{1}{2} = \dfrac{5}{6}$

**16.** Describe and correct the error in solving the equation $1.8 + a = 4.5$.

$$1.8 + a = 4.5$$
$$1.8 + a + 1.8 = 4.5 + 1.8$$
$$a = 6.3$$

**Write the verbal sentence as an equation. Then solve the equation.**

**17.** The difference of a number $b$ and 8 is $-15$.

**18.** 9 more than a number $x$ is 24.

**LESSON**
**4.6**

# Practice *continued*
For use with pages 225–231

**Lesson 4.6**

**Write and solve an equation to find the unknown side length.**

**19.** Perimeter: 12 ft

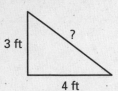

3 ft

?

4 ft

**20.** Perimeter: 11.3 mm

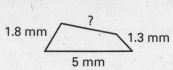

1.8 mm   ?   1.3 mm

5 mm

**21.** Perimeter: 12.3 in.

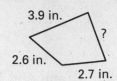

3.9 in.

?

2.6 in.

2.7 in.

**22.** A paperback version of a book costs $17.10. This cost is $2.89 less than the cost of the hardcover version of the book. Write and solve an equation to find the hardcover cost of the book.

**23.** During a recent trip to the gym, you worked out with free weights and rode a stationary bike. You used a stationary bike for 28 minutes of the 75 minutes you spent at the gym. Write and solve an equation to find the number of minutes you spent working out with free weights.

**24.** The left- and right-hand margins on a sheet of paper are both 1.25 inches wide. The total width of the sheet of paper is 8.5 inches. Write and solve an equation to find the width of the text area that lies between the margins.

**LESSON 4.7** **Practice**
For use with pages 233–239

**Tell whether the number is a solution of the equation.**

**1.** $-5r = 125; -15$

**2.** $4.2a = -21; -5$

**3.** $\dfrac{n}{-6} = -84; -14$

**Describe how to solve the equation without actually solving.**

**4.** $8x = 72$

**5.** $-14b = 8$

**6.** $\dfrac{m}{11} = -6$

**Solve the equation. Check your solution.**

**7.** $4p = 48$

**8.** $2.3y = 20.7$

**9.** $\dfrac{1}{5}c = 35$

**10.** $9d = 76.5$

**11.** $\dfrac{m}{7} = -43$

**12.** $\dfrac{z}{6.2} = 4.5$

**13.** $\dfrac{a}{8} = 3.6$

**14.** $9.8 = \dfrac{w}{2.3}$

**15.** $-6 = \dfrac{3}{8}r$

**16.** $\dfrac{5}{3}t = 30$

**17.** $5.3q = 1.431$

**18.** $b + 4b = 8$

**Write the verbal sentence as an equation. Then solve the equation.**

**19.** The quotient of a number $x$ and 6 is 8.7.

**20.** Three times a number $a$ equals 14.4.

# Practice continued
For use with pages 233–239

**21.** The product of 2.2 and a number $m$ is 13.2.

**22.** At a part-time job, Marcus earns $8.50 per hour. Write and solve an equation to find the number of hours he has to work to earn $102.

**23.** It costs you $1.96 for four pounds of bananas. Write and solve an equation to find the cost of one pound of bananas.

**24.** In a survey about favorite book categories, $\frac{1}{4}$ of the total number

of people surveyed, or 39 people, responded that mystery was their favorite category. Write and solve an equation to find the total number of people surveyed.

## LESSON 5.1 Practice
For use with pages 255–259

**Match the statement with its ratio.**

1. shaded squares to unshaded squares          **A.** $20:8$

2. unshaded squares to total squares           **B.** $8:12$

3. total squares to shaded squares             **C.** $12:20$

**The table shows the numbers of wins and losses for two little league baseball teams during a season. Use the table to write the specified ratio.**

4. Dynamos wins to Titans wins

|          | Wins | Losses |
|----------|------|--------|
| **Dynamos** | 13   | 17     |
| **Titans**  | 19   | 11     |

5. Titans wins to Titans losses

6. Dynamos losses to all Dynamos games

**Write the ratio as a fraction in simplest form.**

7. $\dfrac{9}{27}$          8. $\dfrac{18}{24}$          9. $4:70$

10. 35 to 105          11. $22:7$          12. 12 to 165

## LESSON 5.1  Practice *continued*
For use with pages 255–259

**Write the ratio of the first measurement to the second measurement. Write both measurements in the same unit.**

**13.** 60 sec, 2 min

**14.** 2 h, 150 min

**15.** 20 min, 600 sec

**Complete the statement using $<$, $>$, or $=$.**

**16.** $8:10$ ___?___ $4:12$

**17.** $45:36$ ___?___ $15:12$

**18.** $54:78$ ___?___ $64:84$

**Find a value for $x$ that makes the first ratio equivalent to the second ratio.**

**19.** $x$ to 5, 80 to 25

**20.** $x$ to 14, 56 to 98

**21.** $x$ to 117, 4 to 9

**22.** The Roanoke River is 410 miles long, but boats can only travel on, or navigate, 112 miles of the total length. Write the ratio of the Roanoke's navigable length to its total length as a fraction in simplest form.

**23.** There were 156 threatened species of animals and 146 threatened species of plants in the United States in 2006. Write the ratio of threatened species of animals to threatened species of plants as a fraction in simplest form.

**24.** In the 2004 Summer Olympics, Australia earned 17 gold medals, 16 silver medals, and 16 bronze medals. Write the ratio of gold medals to all medals.

## LESSON 5.2 Practice
For use with pages 260–264

1. Describe and correct the error in finding the average speed for an object traveling 4 meters in 20 seconds.

$$\text{Average speed} = \frac{20 \text{ m}}{4 \text{ sec}}$$

$$= \frac{(20 \div 4) \text{ m}}{(4 \div 4) \text{ sec}}$$

$$= \frac{5 \text{ m}}{1 \text{ sec}}$$

## Match the rate with the equivalent unit rate.

2. $\frac{42 \text{ m}}{15 \text{ sec}}$

3. $\frac{72 \text{ m}}{8 \text{ sec}}$

4. $\frac{13 \text{ m}}{4 \text{ sec}}$

A. $\frac{2.8 \text{ m}}{1 \text{ sec}}$

B. $\frac{3.25 \text{ m}}{1 \text{ sec}}$

C. $\frac{9 \text{ m}}{1 \text{ sec}}$

## Find the unit rate.

5. $\frac{16 \text{ L}}{2 \text{ h}}$

6. $\frac{\$54}{6 \text{ lb}}$

7. $\frac{18 \text{ ft}}{5 \text{ sec}}$

8. $28 for 8 people

9. 17 ounces for $5

10. 30 cups for 16 servings

## Find the average speed.

11. 128 inches in 16 hours

12. 34 meters in 10 seconds

13. 384 feet in 4 minutes 16 seconds

14. 184 yards in 3 minutes 4 seconds

Lesson 5.2

**LESSON 5.2** **Practice** *continued*
For use with pages 260–264

**Determine which is the better buy.**

**15.** Salsa: 16 ounces for $3.36 or 24 ounces for $4.80

**16.** Mustard: 12 ounces for $1.56 or 18 ounces for $2.70

**17.** Milk: 2 quarts for $3 or 4 quarts for $5.96

**18.** The gas mileage of a car is the ratio of the number of miles driven to the number of gallons of gasoline used. You use 3 gallons of gasoline to drive a car 84 miles. Write the gas mileage of the car as a unit rate.

**19.** A person's hourly earnings can be described as the ratio of the amount of money earned to the number of hours worked. Wendy earns $450 for working 36 hours in one week. Write her hourly earnings as a unit rate.

**20.** A swimmer completed a 150-meter race in 1 minute and 40 seconds. What was the swimmer's average speed?

Lesson 5.2

**LESSON 5.3** **Practice**
For use with pages 265–271

**Use equivalent ratios to solve the proportion.**

**1.** $\dfrac{x}{21} = \dfrac{6}{7}$

**2.** $\dfrac{3}{b} = \dfrac{24}{88}$

**3.** $\dfrac{18}{81} = \dfrac{p}{9}$

**4.** $\dfrac{33}{45} = \dfrac{11}{r}$

**5.** $\dfrac{y}{13} = \dfrac{60}{156}$

**6.** $\dfrac{18}{14} = \dfrac{c}{21}$

**Use algebra to solve the proportion.**

**7.** $\dfrac{z}{7} = \dfrac{16}{56}$

**8.** $\dfrac{a}{24} = \dfrac{9}{6}$

**9.** $\dfrac{16}{40} = \dfrac{q}{5}$

**10.** $\dfrac{18}{72} = \dfrac{s}{4}$

**11.** $\dfrac{w}{16} = \dfrac{35}{40}$

**12.** $\dfrac{20}{48} = \dfrac{d}{12}$

**13.** Two pounds of apples cost \$3. Describe and correct the error in the proportion used to find the cost $c$ of 18 pounds of apples.

 $\dfrac{2}{3} = \dfrac{c}{18}$

**Write and then solve the proportion.**

**14.** 9 is to 2 as $x$ is to 16.

**15.** 6 is to 20 as 54 is to $b$.

**16.** $m$ is to 18 as 5 is to 90.

**17.** 100 is to 75 as 4 is to $r$.

Lesson 5.3

**18.** In 2005, the average television viewer watched about 32 hours of television in 7 days. About how many hours of television did the average viewer watch in 28 days?

**19.** Carbon is one of the building blocks of human cells. A 150-pound person's body contains 27 pounds of carbon. Assuming that the ratio of the number of pounds of carbon in a person to his or her weight is the same for every person, how many pounds of carbon are in a 120-pound person?

**20.** A recipe that makes 8 pints of coleslaw uses 2 heads of cabbage. How many pints of coleslaw can be made from 5 heads of cabbage?

**21.** A modem transfers 512 kilobytes of data in 4 seconds. At this rate, how long does it take to transfer 7680 kilobytes of data?

Lesson 5.3

Name _____  Date _____

**Use the cross products property to solve the proportion.**

1. $\dfrac{x}{6} = \dfrac{6}{4}$

2. $\dfrac{8}{2} = \dfrac{24}{b}$

3. $\dfrac{18}{t} = \dfrac{3}{5}$

4. $\dfrac{3}{7} = \dfrac{q}{28}$

5. $\dfrac{y}{6.6} = \dfrac{5}{11}$

6. $\dfrac{3}{5.5} = \dfrac{6}{d}$

7. $\dfrac{2}{n} = \dfrac{40}{65}$

8. $\dfrac{1}{4} = \dfrac{c}{17}$

9. $\dfrac{15.2}{19} = \dfrac{z}{2.5}$

10. Describe and correct the error in solving the proportion $\dfrac{3}{5} = \dfrac{x}{24}$.

$$\dfrac{3}{5} = \dfrac{x}{24}$$

$$3 \cdot x = 5 \cdot 24$$

$$x = 40$$

**Write and then solve the proportion.**

11. 21 is to $y$ as 7 is to 15.

12. 2.4 is to 3.6 as $x$ is to 12.

13. 14 is to 6 as $m$ is to 10.2.

14. 3.2 is to 4.1 as 9.6 is to $p$.

**LESSON 5.4** **Practice** *continued*
For use with pages 274–280

**Tell whether the ratios form a proportion.**

**15.** $\dfrac{20}{75}, \dfrac{4}{15}$ 　　　　**16.** $\dfrac{8}{9}, \dfrac{36}{32}$ 　　　　**17.** $\dfrac{1.2}{3.4}, \dfrac{6}{17}$

**18.** Leslie can read about 2192 words in 8 minutes. About how many words can she read in 60 minutes?

**19.** A filter for an aquarium cleans 800 gallons of water in 60 minutes. How many gallons of water does the filter clean in 4.5 minutes?

**20.** There are 2 grams of fiber in 0.25 cup of raisins. How many cups of raisins are needed to get 5 grams of fiber?

**21.** The national flag of France has a width-to-length ratio of 2 : 3. What is the perimeter of an 18-inch long French flag?

**22.** Florence spent a total of $1.25 to park her car on the street. One quarter buys 15 minutes of parking time on the parking meter. At most, how long can she park?

**The scale on a map is 1 cm : 12 km. Find the actual distance in kilometers for the given length on the map.**

**1.** 4 cm                     **2.** 7.25 cm                    **3.** 11.25 cm

**Models of buildings in Detroit, Michigan were created by using a scale of 1 in. : 50 ft. Find the height of the model in inches for the given height of the building.**

**4.** Marriott Hotel: 725 ft

**5.** Book Tower: 472 ft

**6.** Madden Building: 470 ft

**7.** ANR Building: 430 ft

**8.** Which scale is equivalent to 1 m : 25 m?
    **A.** 1 : 25                    **B.** 1 : 2500                    **C.** 1 : 25,000

**Write the ratio as a scale in simplest form.**

**9.** $\frac{5 \text{ ft}}{30 \text{ ft}}$                  **10.** $\frac{42 \text{ in.}}{12 \text{ in.}}$                  **11.** $\frac{0.3 \text{ yd}}{3 \text{ yd}}$

Name _____

Date _____

**Practice** continued
For use with pages 281–286

CA Standards
NS 1.3

## Find the scale used to create the model.

**12.** The scale model of a 72-inch long table is 8 inches long.

**13.** The scale model of an 84-inch long couch is 7 inches long.

**14.** The scale model of a 45-inch tall bookcase is 2.5 inches tall.

**15.** The scale model of a 40-inch tall chair is 1.25 inches tall.

**16.** The table shows some common scales used in model railroading. For each scale, find the length of a model of an 82-foot long boxcar. Give the length of each model in feet and round your answers to the nearest hundredth.

| Scale Name | Scale |
|------------|-------|
| N | 1 : 160 |
| S | 1 : 64 |
| O | 1 : 48 |

**17.** The scale 1 in. : 120 ft was used to create a 169.3-inch tall model of Alaska's Mount McKinley. Estimate the height of Mount McKinley from the height of the model.

Name _____ Date _____

## LESSON 6.1 Practice
For use with pages 301–304

 CA Standard
Gr. 5 NS 1.2

Lesson 6.1

**Write the percent as a fraction.**

**1.** 88%                **2.** 48%                **3.** 10%

**4.** 75%                **5.** 2%                 **6.** 39%

**Write the fraction as a percent.**

**7.** $\frac{4}{5}$                **8.** $\frac{3}{10}$                **9.** $\frac{29}{50}$

**10.** $\frac{9}{20}$                **11.** $\frac{14}{25}$                **12.** $\frac{1}{5}$

**Find the percent of the number.**

**13.** 40% of 85                **14.** 25% of 64                **15.** 10% of 150

**16.** 70% of 30                **17.** 50% of 400                **18.** 15% of 200

**Tell whether the statement is *true* or *false*. If it is false, correct the statement.**

**19.** $\frac{1}{10} = 1\%$                **20.** $\frac{43}{50} = 86\%$                **21.** $\frac{17}{20} = 34\%$

**California Math, Course 1**          **71**
Chapter 6    Practice Workbook

**LESSON
6.1**

**Practice** *continued*
For use with pages 301–304

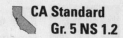

Lesson 6.1

**Solve the proportion by writing the fraction as a percent.**

**22.** $\frac{7}{20} = \frac{x}{100}$     **23.** $\frac{21}{25} = \frac{y}{100}$     **24.** $\frac{33}{50} = \frac{v}{100}$

**Complete the statement using $<$, $>$, or $=$.**

**25.** 20% of 90 __?__ 25% of 100          **26.** 12% of 350 __?__ 12% of 250

**27.** Only 40% of people between the ages of 18 and 24 read a daily newspaper. Write the percent as a fraction in simplest form.

**28.** Seven out of every 20 homes that own at least one television have two televisions. What percent of the homes that own at least one television have two televisions?

**29.** Five of the 100 seniors at your school are on the yearbook staff. What percent of your school's seniors are not on the yearbook staff?

Name _____  Date _____

# Practice
For use with pages 305–311

CA Standard
NS 1.4

**Complete the proportion. Then answer the question.**

1. What number is 75% of 320?

   $$\frac{a}{?} = \frac{?}{100}$$

2. What percent of 40 is 4?

   $$\frac{?}{?} = \frac{p}{100}$$

3. Describe and correct the error when using a proportion to answer the question.

   50 is 20% of what number?

   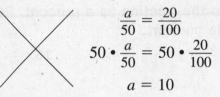

**Match the question with the correct proportion.**

4. 75 is 12% of what number?       **A.** $\frac{12}{75} = \frac{p}{100}$

5. What number is 12% of 75?       **B.** $\frac{75}{b} = \frac{12}{100}$

6. What percent of 75 is 12?       **C.** $\frac{a}{75} = \frac{12}{100}$

**Use a proportion to answer the question.**

7. What percent of 50 is 5?

8. What percent of 75 is 21?

9. 68 is 85% of what number?

10. 40 is 32% of what number?

**LESSON 6.2** **Practice** *continued*
For use with pages 305–311

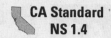

**11.** What number is 15% of 80?

**12.** What number is 40% of 95?

**13.** What percent of 60 is 27?

**14.** 18 is 6% of what number?

**Write the fraction as a percent. Round your answer to the nearest whole percent.**

**15.** $\frac{1}{9}$

**16.** $\frac{2}{11}$

**17.** $\frac{3}{13}$

**18.** You have 45 books on your bookshelf. If 9 are mystery books, what percent of the books on your bookshelf are mystery books?

**19.** Five percent of Ireland's total area is forest and woodland. The total area of Ireland is 70,280 square kilometers. How many square kilometers of Ireland's area are forest and woodland?

**20.** Forty-five percent of the trees in a park are maple trees. There are 27 maple trees in the park. How many trees are in the park in all?

## LESSON 6.3 Practice
For use with pages 312–317

**Draw a model for the percent.**

**1.** 44%

**2.** 4.5%

**3.** 112%

**Write the percent as a decimal.**

**4.** 34%

**5.** 2%

**6.** 175%

**7.** 0.8%

**8.** 27.9%

**9.** 6.25%

**Write the decimal as a percent.**

**10.** 0.29

**11.** 0.05

**12.** 0.308

**13.** 4.132

**14.** 17.04

**15.** 0.00688

**Write the fraction as a percent. Round to the nearest tenth of a percent.**

**16.** $\frac{7}{18}$

**17.** $\frac{15}{21}$

**18.** $\frac{5}{34}$

**19.** $\frac{24}{45}$

**20.** $\frac{13}{54}$

**21.** $\frac{22}{95}$

Lesson 6.3

# Practice *continued*
For use with pages 312–317

**Complete the statement using $<$, $>$, or $=$.**

**22.** 0.25% __?__ 0.025　　　　**23.** 8.1 __?__ 81%　　　　**24.** 0.034 __?__ 3.4%

**25.** In 1960, a farmer was paid $1 for one bushel of corn. In 2000, the price of one bushel of corn was 185% of the 1960 price. How much was a farmer paid for one bushel of corn in 2000?

**26.** About 0.6% of Nebraska's total area is water. The total area of Nebraska is 77,354 square miles. How many square miles of Nebraska's total area is water?

**27.** The cost of airmailing a 60-ounce package to Mexico is 3050% of the cost of airmailing a 1-ounce package to Mexico. It costs $.60 to airmail a 1-ounce package. How much does it cost to airmail a 60-ounce package?

**LESSON 6.4**
# Practice
For use with pages 319–324

## Match the question with the correct equation.

**1.** 94 is 17% of what number?     **A.** $a = 0.17 \cdot 94$

**2.** What percent of 94 is 17?     **B.** $94 = 0.17 \cdot b$

**3.** What number is 17% of 94?     **C.** $17 = p\% \cdot 94$

**4.** Which expression would you use to estimate 36% of 84?

    **A.** 30% of 84

    **B.** 25% of 84

    **C.** 40% of 84

    **D.** 35% of 84

## Use the percent equation to answer the question.

**5.** What number is 25% of 600?     **6.** What number is 70% of 180?

**7.** 174 is what percent of 600?     **8.** 12 is what percent of 80?

**9.** 52 is what percent of 80?     **10.** 28 is 28% of what number?

**Practice** *continued*
For use with pages 319–324

**11.** 90 is 8% of what number?

**12.** What number is 52% of 500?

**13.** 178 is what percent of 200?

**14.** 45 is 60% of what number?

**15.** Which is greater, 35% of 60 or 30% of 80?

**16.** In 2005, the population of Ohio was about 3.8% of the population of the entire United States. The population of the United States in 2005 was about 295,507,000 people. What was Ohio's population in 2005?

**17.** In 2004, there were 653 evening newspapers in the United States. This is about 44.8% of the number of evening newspapers in the United States in 1960. How many evening newspapers were there in 1960? Round your answer to the nearest whole number.

**18.** In 2005, there were about 2,100,990 farms in the United States. Twenty-four thousand three hundred of the farms were in South Carolina. What percent of the farms were in South Carolina? Round your answer to the nearest whole percent.

**19.** You receive an 8% commission on furniture sales. On Saturday, you received $188 in commission. How much furniture did you sell on Saturday?

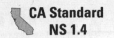

CA Standard
NS 1.4

## LESSON 6.5 Practice
For use with pages 325–329

**1.** Which expression will give the new price of a $15 item marked up by 28%?

    **A.** $28 + 0.15 \times 28$

    **B.** $28 - 0.15 \times 28$

    **C.** $15 + 0.28 \times 15$

    **D.** $15 - 0.28 \times 15$

### Use the given information to find the new price.

**2.** Original price: $42
  Discount: 15%

**3.** Original price: $62
  Discount: 30%

**4.** Wholesale price: $120
  Markup: 10%

**5.** Wholesale price: $225
  Markup: 18%

**6.** Food bill before tax: $24
  Sales tax: 6%

**7.** Food bill before tip: $35
  Tip: 18%

**8.** Original price: $78
  Discount: 12%

**9.** Wholesale price: $218
  Markup: 33%

**10.** Food bill before tax: $54
  Sales tax: 7%

**11.** Describe and correct the error in finding the total cost of a $49 meal
with 6% sales tax and an 18% tip.

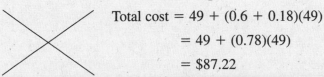

    Total cost $= 49 + (0.6 + 0.18)(49)$

                   $= 49 + (0.78)(49)$

                   $= \$87.22$

### Find the total cost.

**12.** A meal is $32 with 5% sales tax and a 20% tip.

**13.** An item is $55 with a 20% discount and 5% sales tax.

# Practice *continued*
For use with pages 325–329

**14.** An item is $82 with a 30% discount and 7% sales tax.

**15.** You buy two DVDs at the video store. One DVD is $21.49 and the other DVD is $19.99, but is on sale for 15% off the original price. How much do you spend on both DVDs? Round your answer to the nearest cent.

**16.** The markup on a digital camera is 125%. The wholesale price of the digital camera is $97. What is the retail price?

**17.** At a restaurant, you order a lunch that costs $6.50 and a beverage that costs $1.50. You leave a 20% tip and the sales tax is 7%. What is the total cost?

**LESSON 6.6** **Practice**
For use with pages 331–335

CA Standard NS 1.4

*Lesson 6.6*

1. Which expression could be used to find the balance of an account that started with $115 and earned 4% interest for 8 months?

   **A.** $115 + (115)(0.04)(8)$

   **B.** $115 + (115)(4)(8)$

   **C.** $115 + (115)(0.04)\left(\frac{8}{12}\right)$

**For an account that earns simple annual interest, find the interest and the balance of the account.**

2. $375 at 4% for 5 years

3. $278 at 8% for 9 months

4. $2300 at 2.2% for 6 months

5. $4880 at 3.8% for 3 months

6. $1800 at 13.5% for 4 months

7. $600 at 4.5% for 24 months

8. Describe and correct the error in finding the amount of time it takes $1400 to earn $350 in interest at a 10% interest rate.

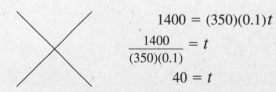

$$1400 = (350)(0.1)t$$
$$\frac{1400}{(350)(0.1)} = t$$
$$40 = t$$

**Use the simple interest formula to find the unknown quantity.**

9. $I = \underline{\ ?\ }$
   $P = \$4000$
   $r = 4.5\%$
   $t = 5$ years

10. $I = \$67.50$
    $P = \underline{\ ?\ }$
    $r = 3\%$
    $t = 3$ years

11. $I = \$1104$
    $P = \$4600$
    $r = \underline{\ ?\ }$
    $t = 4$ years

**12.** $I = \$3621.20$
$P = \$8230$
$r = 5.5\%$
$t = \underline{\ ?\ }$

**13.** $I = \underline{\ ?\ }$
$P = \$378$
$r = 2\%$
$t = 6$ years

**14.** $I = \$13.98$
$P = \underline{\ ?\ }$
$r = 3.6\%$
$t = 4$ months

**15.** You deposit $425 into a money market account for three months. The account earns 2.5% simple interest. How much money is in the account after three months? Round your answer to the nearest cent.

**16.** You put $1000 into a six-month certificate of deposit. After the six-month period, your balance is $1012.50. What was the simple annual interest rate?

**17.** You deposit $4000 into a savings account. The account earns 2.75% simple interest. How long will it take to earn $220 in interest?

Name _____   Date _____

LESSON
**7.1**

# Practice
For use with pages 353-358

CA Standards
SDAP 2.1
SDAP 2.2

**Decide whether it makes sense to survey a sample to collect the data. Explain your reasoning.**

**1.** The ticket sales of 5 teams in a professional sports division

**2.** The ages of students who ride the bus to school

**3.** The favorite type of food of residents in the United States

**4.** The ages of the 8 students in the chess club

**You survey people at school about expanding the teacher's parking lot. Identify the sampling method. Tell whether the sample is likely to be biased.**

**5.** Survey people as they leave the building

**6.** Survey every third teacher in an alphabetical list

**7.** Survey all of your teachers

**8.** Place a questionnaire in the main hallway of the school

Lesson 7.1

## LESSON 7.1 **Practice** *continued*
For use with pages 353–358

**Identify the population. Describe a sampling method that is likely to result in a representative sample.**

**9.** A class president wants to know whether students favor a 5 year class reunion or a 10 year class reunion.

**10.** A restaurant owner wants to know the favorite appetizer of regular customers.

**11.** Jeffrey wants to find the percent of sixth and seventh grade students that walk to his school every morning. A survey of each student in his sixth grade classes shows that 21 of the 74 students walk to school.

  **a.** Identify the population, the sample, and the sampling method.

  **b.** A random sampling of seventh grade students shows that about 30% of the students walk to school. Compare the seventh grade results to the sixth grade results.

**12.** Management at a gym wants to find out what they can do to improve the facilities for all of their members. They consider conducting a survey using systematic sampling of the female members. Is the sample likely to be representative? Explain.

# Practice
For use with pages 359–363

**Tell whether the question could produce biased results. If so, explain why and rewrite the question so that it is not biased.**

**1.** How often do you play golf?

**2.** Would you rather watch a winless baseball team play today or relax on the beach?

**3.** Do you prefer to listen to music at a normal volume or at an excessively loud volume?

**4.** Do you agree with the government's policy on the environment?

**The given claim about students is invalid. Explain why the survey described might have led to this invalid claim.**

  **Claim:** Most students fall asleep by 9 P.M.

**5.** Students were surveyed in front of a parent.

**6.** Random students leaving school were asked, "What time do you usually fall asleep, keeping in mind that most of your friends fell asleep at 9 P.M. last night?"

**7.** Students were surveyed only if they arrived between 45 minutes and 30 minutes before school started.

**LESSON 7.2** **Practice** continued
For use with pages 359–363

8. Parents were surveyed in front of other parents.

9. You randomly survey friends about their favorite sport. You ask, "Which sport is your favorite, including baseball, our national pastime?" The results are displayed below.

| Sport | Basketball | Football | Baseball | Other |
|-------|-----------|----------|----------|-------|
| Votes | 3 | 7 | 14 | 10 |

You claim that baseball is the favorite sport of your friends. Is the claim valid? Explain your reasoning.

10. An elementary school teacher asked students to vote whether to go outside for recess or stay inside. Just before the vote, the teacher told the class that she would be voting to stay inside. The class voted aloud and staying inside got the most votes. Do you think the result is valid? Explain your reasoning.

Lesson 7.2

**LESSON 7.3  Practice**
For use with pages 364–369

1. Identify which of the following values is the mean of the data.

   Data:  14, 15, 24, 18, 14, 17

   **A.** 14          **B.** 15          **C.** 16          **D.** 17

**Find the mean, median, and mode(s) of the data.**

2. 12, 25, 23, 17, 23

3. 7, 3, 9, 2, 7, 2

4. 22, 36, 9, 27, 30, 20

5. 113, 249, 312, 113, 113

6. 1, 1, 7, 3, 2, 2, 3, 5

7. 24, 3, 18, 90, 30, 13, 18

**Describe how including the new value in the data set will affect the mean, median, and mode.**

8. 7, 7, 13, new value: 17

9. 2, 5, 3, 8, new value: 2

10. 13, 2, 12, 7, new value: 1.5

11. 5, 5, 9, 5, 4, new value: 2

12. 20, 10, 10, 14, new value: 14

13. 0, 2.5, 6.5, 4, 8, new value: 4.2

**Practice** continued
For use with pages 364–369

**The high temperatures, in degrees Fahrenheit, for a city during a week in June are listed below.**

70, 73, 94, 69, 72, 71, 69

**14.** Find the mean, median, and mode(s) of the data.

**15.** Which measure is most useful for describing the typical data value? Explain.

**In Exercises 16–18, use the following information. A car dealer claims that the average car sold is $53,000. The numbers listed below are the prices of the cars that have been sold.**

$53,000, $12,000, $17,000, $21,000, $53,000, $9,000

**16.** Find the mean, median, and mode(s) of the prices.

**17.** Is the car dealers claim justified? Why or why not?

**18.** Why would the car dealer claim $53,000 as the average car price?

Lesson 7.3

**LESSON 7.4**

# Practice

For use with pages 371–377

CA Standards
SDAP 1.1
SDAP 1.3

**Find the median, extremes, quartiles, range, and interquartile range of the data.**

**1.** 45, 46, 91, 72, 79, 80, 48, 52, 9, 74

**2.** 33, 14, 16, 40, 44, 7, 25, 16, 34, 31

**3.** 4.2, 6.2, 4.9, 3.4, 4.4, 2.1, 3.6, 5.5

**4.** 401, 255, 347, 499, 458, 320

**Compare the mean, median, mode(s), and range of the data set**
***with*** **and** ***without*** **the outlier in bold.**

**5.** 35, 30, 38, 52, **82,** 38, 47

**6.** 28, 36, **1,** 36, 37, 30, 31, 33

**7.** 230, 190, 290, 300, **48,** 204, 250

**8.** 85, 88, 62, 60, **120,** 81, 38, 90

**Find the median, extremes, quartiles, range, and interquartile range of the data in the box-and-whisker plot.**

**9.**

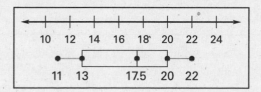

**10.**

**LESSON**
**7.4**

**Practice** *continued*
For use with pages 371–377

CA Standards
SDAP 1.1
SDAP 1.3

**11.** The box-and-whisker plots show the spread of the ages of students in a college class. The data in the upper box-and-whisker plot include the outliers.

Describe how the *exclusion* of the outliers from the data, shown in the lower box-and-whisker plot, affects the median and range of the data.

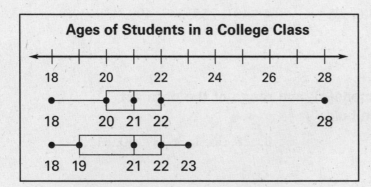

**LESSON 7.5** **Practice**
For use with pages 379–384

**Make a frequency table of the data. Then make a histogram of the data.**

1. **Total points scored in football games:** 78, 26, 69, 37, 37, 73, 58, 37, 69, 48, 85, 27, 36, 37, 37, 73, 50, 54, 38, 28, 29

2. **Magnitudes of major earthquakes from 1998 through 2001:** 6.1, 6.6, 6.9, 6.3, 7.1, 6.4, 7.4, 5.8, 7.6, 4.6, 7.5, 5.9, 7.5, 5.3, 8.0, 5.1, 4.9, 5.8, 7.5, 6.8, 7.7, 7.7, 6.6, 5.4, 6.8, 8.4

3. **Minimum heights for amusement park rides:** 48, 42, 48, 36, 48, 46, 42, 48, 48, 46, 48, 48, 48, 46, 48, 36, 48, 48, 46, 46, 46, 48, 46, 36, 39, 46

4. The total numbers of songs on different CDs are given below. Describe and correct the error(s) in the frequency table.

   12, 8, 11, 12, 11, 8, 5, 8, 10, 11, 14, 11, 9, 8, 6, 13, 14, 11, 14, 12, 10, 10, 10, 18, 20, 6

| Interval | Tally | Frequency |
|----------|-------|-----------|
| 5–9 | ЖНТ III | 8 |
| 9–13 | ЖНТ ЖНТ III | 13 |
| 13–17 | ЖНТ ЖНТ | 10 |
| 17–20 | II | 2 |

**LESSON 7.5** **Practice** *continued*
For use with pages 379–384

5. Which intervals can be used to make a frequency table of the data?

32, 38, 49, 25, 31, 31, 56, 24, 28, 58, 25, 31, 40, 52, 61, 52, 34, 27, 69, 63, 45

   **A.** 0–10, 11–20, 21–30, 31–40, 41–50, 51–60, 61–70

   **B.** 25–35, 35–45, 45–55, 55–65, 65–75

   **C.** 20–30, 31–40, 41–50, 51–60, 61–70

   **D.** 21–30, 31–40, 41–50, 51–60, 61–70

**The days of the month in January and February of 2003 on which the New York Philharmonic was scheduled to perform are given below.**

2, 3, 7, 9, 11, 12, 14, 16, 17, 18, 22, 23, 24, 25, 30, 31, 1, 14, 19, 20, 21, 22, 26, 27, 28

6. Make a histogram of the data.

7. Make a conclusion about the data.

## LESSON 7.6 Practice
For use with pages 385–391

**In Exercises 1–3, use the circle graph that shows the results of a survey that asked students to name their favorite pet.**

1. What percent of students named dogs or cats as their favorite pet?

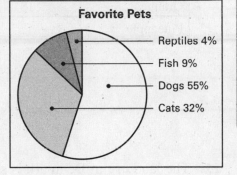

**Favorite Pets**

- Reptiles 4%
- Fish 9%
- Dogs 55%
- Cats 32%

2. What percent of students did not name fish as their favorite pet?

3. Find the angle measure of the section that represents the students who named dogs as their favorite pet.

**Find the angle measure that corresponds to the percent of a circle.**

4. 17.5%         5. 22.5%         6. 32.5%

**Display the survey data in a circle graph.**

7.

| Getting to School | Students |
|---|---|
| Walk | 30% |
| Ride bicycle | 25% |
| Ride bus | 40% |
| Ride with parents | 5% |

8.

| Favorite Shirt | Students |
|---|---|
| T-Shirt | 25% |
| Sweater | 35% |
| Button-down | 30% |
| Sweatshirt | 10% |

Lesson 7.6

## LESSON 7.6

# Practice *continued*
For use with pages 385–391

9.

| Favorite Juice | People |
|----------------|--------|
| Apple | 6 |
| Grape | 14 |
| Orange | 18 |
| Pineapple | 2 |

10.

| Collecting Items | People |
|------------------|--------|
| Baseball cards | 44 |
| Stamps | 8 |
| Coins | 16 |
| Dolls | 12 |

11. The land use in Denmark is shown below. Display the data in a circle graph. Make a conclusion about the data in your graph.

| Denmark Land Use | | | |
|---|---|---|---|
| **Type of Use** | Arable land | Meadows and Pastures | Forest and woodland | Other |
| **Percent** | 60% | 5% | 10% | 25% |

Name _____ Date _____

**Choose one or more appropriate data displays for the data.
Explain your choice(s).**

**1.** The percent of people surveyed who prefer wheat bread from a list of bread types

**2.** The change in enrollment at a college over the last 10 years

**3.** Which data display would be most appropriate for the data below?

| Mean Earnings in 2003 for Women with a Bachelor's Degree or Higher | | | | | |
|---|---|---|---|---|---|
| Age | 25–34 | 35–44 | 45–54 | 55–64 | 65 and over |
| Earnings | $40,977 | $46,495 | $48,526 | $46,051 | $25,354 |

   **A.** Box-and-whisker plot        **B.** Histogram

   **C.** Bar graph                   **D.** Line plot

**Decide whether or not to use a broken scale to make a line graph
of the data. Then make a line graph of the data.**

**4.**

| Number of tickets purchased | 8 | 10 | 12 | 14 |
|---|---|---|---|---|
| Cost | 48 | 60 | 72 | 84 |

**5.**

| Year | 1 | 2 | 3 | 4 |
|---|---|---|---|---|
| Miles on car (in thousands) | 12 | 27 | 45 | 70 |

**LESSON 7.7**  **Practice** *continued*
For use with pages 392–399

6. The bar graph at the right shows the average precipitation in inches in London, England for three different months. Beth claims that the average precipitation in September is two times the average precipitation in July. Tell whether her claim is valid. If not, make a valid claim.

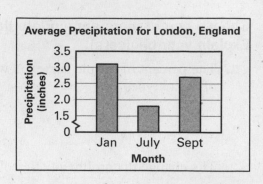

7. Explain why the line graph for the population of Omaha, Nebraska could be misleading. Create a line graph for the data that is not misleading.

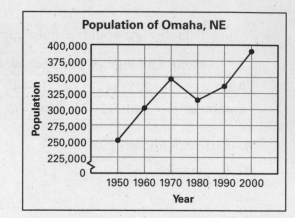

| Year | Population |
|------|------------|
| 1950 | 251,117 |
| 1960 | 301,598 |
| 1970 | 347,000 |
| 1980 | 314,000 |
| 1990 | 335,795 |
| 2000 | 390,007 |

Name _____ Date _____

In Exercises 1–3, use the spinner shown, which is divided
into equal parts. Find the probability of the event. Write the
probability as a fraction, a decimal, and a percent.

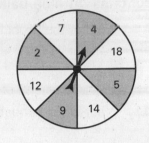

1. Pointer lands on an odd number.

2. Pointer lands on a number that is divisible by 2.

3. Pointer lands on a number that is a multiple of 9.

4. The outcomes on the spinner shown are equally likely. You spin
   the spinner 40 times. Predict the number of spins that will land
   on the number 7.

Each letter in **MASSACHUSETTS** is written on a separate piece
of paper and put into a bag. You randomly choose a piece of
paper from the bag. Find the probability of the event. Write the
probability as a fraction.

5. You choose a T.                    6. You choose an N.

You randomly choose a shape from the shapes below. Find the
probability of choosing the given shape. Write the probability
as a fraction.

7. Sun                    8. Moon                    9. Star

Lesson 8.1

# Practice *continued*
For use with pages 415–420

**In Exercises 10 and 11, use the following information. A bag contains 46 blue balloons, 29 red balloons, and 25 purple balloons.**

**10.** What is the probability that you randomly choose a red balloon?

**11.** What is the probability that you randomly choose a purple balloon?

**In Exercises 12 and 13, use the following information. In your backpack, you have a bag where you keep your pens. There are 8 red pens, 3 blue pens, 4 black pens, and 2 green pens in the bag.**

**12.** What is the probability that you randomly choose a red pen from the bag?

**13.** What is the probability that you randomly choose a blue or black pen from the bag?

**LESSON 8.2** **Practice**
For use with pages 421–426

CA Standards
SDAP 3.2

1. You roll a number cube 100 times. The results are given in the table below. Find the experimental probability of rolling a 6.

| Number | 1 | 2 | 3 | 4 | 5 | 6 |
|---|---|---|---|---|---|---|
| Times rolled | 17 | 15 | 20 | 16 | 14 | 18 |

**In Exercises 2-4, use the information in the table below to find the experimental probability that a student will randomly choose a flavor of milk from the school cafeteria.**

| Flavor of milk | |
|---|---|
| Plain | 57 |
| Chocolate | 72 |
| Strawberry | 21 |

2. What is the experimental probability that a student will randomly choose chocolate milk?

3. What is the experimental probability that a student will randomly choose strawberry milk?

4. What is the experimental probability that a student will *not* randomly choose plain milk?

Lesson 8.2

Name _____  Date _____

**Torry played on a baseball team last year. He had a total of 235 at-bats. The results of his at-bats are shown in the table. Find the experimental probability that the event will occur this year.**

5. He will hit a single.

6. He will strike out.

| Result | Outcome |
|--------|---------|
| single | 39 |
| double | 19 |
| triple | 8 |
| home run | 5 |

| Result | Outcome |
|--------|---------|
| error | 12 |
| strike out | 41 |
| fly out | 60 |
| ground out | 51 |

7. He will hit either a double or a triple.

8. He will get a fly out or a ground out.

9. He will get a hit.

10. The table at the right shows the results of tossing a coin 30 times. What is the experimental probability that the coin lands on tails?

| Result | heads | tails |
|--------|-------|-------|
| **Times tossed** | 16 | 14 |

Name _____    Date _____

**LESSON 8.3**

# Practice

For use with pages 427–432

CA Standards
SDAP 3.3
SDAP 3.4

**Tell whether the events are *disjoint* or *overlapping*.**

1. **Event A:** A person knows how to skateboard.
   **Event B:** A person doesn't know how to skateboard.

2. **Event A:** A person lives in Boston.
   **Event B:** A person lives in Massachusetts.

3. **Event A:** A number is less than 10 and odd.
   **Event B:** A number is divisible by 3.

**Events A and B are disjoint events. Find P(A or B).**

4. $P(A) = 0.32$      5. $P(A) = 0.18$      6. $P(A) = 30\%$
   $P(B) = 0.15$         $P(B) = 0.25$         $P(B) = 9\%$

**Use *P*(not A) to find *P*(A).**

7. $P(\text{not A}) = 0.63$      8. $P(\text{not A}) = \frac{2}{3}$      9. $P(\text{not A}) = 92\%$

Lesson 8.3

LESSON
**8.3**

# Practice *continued*

For use with pages 427–432

**In Exercises 10–13, use the circle graph that shows the percent of sales for each kind of music at a record store. Find the probability that a randomly chosen person who bought music at the store bought the specified kind of music.**

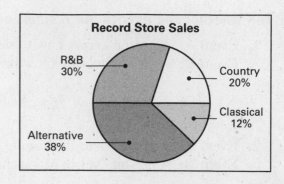

**Record Store Sales**

R&B
30%

Country
20%

Classical
12%

Alternative
38%

**10.** Bought R&B or alternative

**11.** Bought classical or country

**12.** Didn't buy alternative

**13.** Didn't buy classical

**14.** At a dinner, 5 people ordered chicken, 6 people ordered fish, and 12 people ordered vegetable lasagna. A person is randomly chosen and asked what he or she ordered. What is the probability that the person ordered chicken or fish?

Lesson 8.3

**LESSON 8.4**

# Practice
For use with pages 434–439

**Make a table to find the number of
outcomes of the event involving the spinner(s).
Each spinner is divided into equal parts.**

1. Spin spinner B two times.

Spinner A

Spinner B

2. Spin spinner A and spinner B.

3. Spin spinner A two times.

4. A buyer is purchasing mailing envelopes for an office. The
envelopes come in white or tan, and come in sizes of 6 inches by
11 inches, 8.5 inches by 11 inches, and 10.5 inches by 15 inches.
The buyer can also choose between unpadded envelopes, padded
envelopes, or bubble-lined envelopes. Make a tree diagram to find
all of the possible envelope combinations.

5. A deli has an option to create your own sandwich. Your bread
choices are white, whole wheat, or rye. You can choose between
ham, turkey, or tuna fish as a sandwich filling and American,
cheddar, Swiss, or provolone as a cheese topping. Make a tree
diagram to find all of the possible sandwich combinations.

6. A department store stocks bed sheets that come in four sizes: king,
queen, full, and twin. All sheets are made of flannel or cotton, and
you can get any of the sheets in a solid color, in a striped pattern, or
in a flowered pattern. Make a tree diagram to find all of the possible
sheet combinations.

*Lesson 8.4*

# Practice *continued*
For use with pages 434–439

**A store sells a grab bag of three travel-sized games. A bag
contains one of the following books: a book of crossword puzzles,
a book of word searches, or a book of word scrambles. The bag
also contains a checkers game or a chess game and one of the
following games: a tile game, a board game, or a drawing game.
Use a tree diagram to find the probability of the event.**

**7.** A bag will contain the word scramble book.

**8.** A bag will contain the crossword puzzle book and the drawing game.

**Suppose that you roll two number cubes. Use a table to find the
probability of the event.**

**9.** Both numbers are even.

**10.** You roll a 2 and a 4.

**LESSON 8.5** **Practice**
For use with pages 441–446

**Tell whether the events are *independent* or *dependent*.**

**1.** You roll a number cube two times. The first time you roll a 2 and the second time you roll a 1.

**2.** You randomly choose a password from a list of words. Then your friend randomly chooses a password from the remaining words.

**Events A and B are independent. Find the unknown probability.**

**3.** $P(A) = 0.7$
$P(B) = 0.2$
$P(A \text{ and } B) = \underline{\quad?\quad}$

**4.** $P(A) = 0.5$
$P(B) = \underline{\quad?\quad}$
$P(A \text{ and } B) = 0.15$

**5.** $P(A) = \underline{\quad?\quad}$
$P(B) = 0.6$
$P(A \text{ and } B) = 0.48$

**Events A and B are dependent. Find the unknown probability.**

**6.** $P(A) = 0.35$
$P(B \text{ given } A) = 0.6$
$P(A \text{ and } B) = \underline{\quad?\quad}$

**7.** $P(A) = 0.3$
$P(B \text{ given } A) = \underline{\quad?\quad}$
$P(A \text{ and } B) = 0.12$

**8.** $P(A) = \underline{\quad?\quad}$
$P(B \text{ given } A) = 0.2$
$P(A \text{ and } B) = 0.04$

**Each letter in the word DIVISION is written on a separate piece of paper. You randomly choose letters one at a time, but you do not replace them. Find the probability that both events A and B will occur.**

**9.** **Event A:** The first letter you choose is an I.

**Event B:** The second letter you choose is an I.

**10.** **Event A:** The first letter you choose is a vowel.

**Event B:** The second letter you choose is a consonant.

Lesson 8.5

| LESSON
8.5 | **Practice** *continued*
For use with pages 441–446 |

**In Exercises 11 and 12, tell whether the situation describes** *independent events* **or** *dependent events*. **Then answer the question.**

**11.** A bag contains 18 blue, 24 red, and 30 yellow balloons. You randomly choose a balloon from the bag, but you do not replace it. Then you randomly choose another balloon. What is the probability that both balloons are blue?

**12.** You have created a computer program that randomly selects a number from 1 to 20. You run the program two times. What is the probability that the program selects 5 as the first number and 7 as the second number?

**LESSON 9.1** **Practice**
For use with pages 463–467

CA Standards
MG 2.1
MG 2.2

**Estimate to classify the angle as** *acute, right, obtuse,* **or** *straight.*

1.
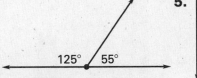

2.
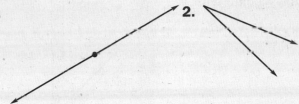

3.
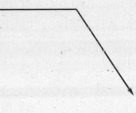

**Tell whether the angles are** *complementary, supplementary,* **or** *neither.* **Explain your reasoning.**

4.
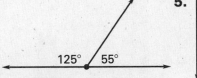
125°  55°

5.

35°  35°

6.
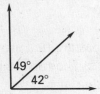
49°
42°

**For the given angle measure, find the measure of a supplementary angle and the measure of a complementary angle, if possible.**

**7.** 17°

**8.** 86°

**9.** 134°

**10.** 59°

**11.** 111°

**12.** 4°

**Find the measure of the angle.**

**13.** $\angle R$ and $\angle S$ are supplementary. If $m\angle R = 65°$, what is $m\angle S$?

**14.** $\angle U$ and $\angle V$ are complementary. If $m\angle U = 28°$, what is $m\angle V$?

| LESSON<br>9.1 | **Practice** *continued*<br>For use with pages 463–467 |

**15.** The angle between the shaft of a golf club and the golf club face is called the *loft angle*. The diagram shows a club with a 44° loft angle. What is the value of *x*?

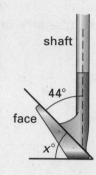

**16.** Sometimes ropes are tied around a tree so that it grows straight upward. The rope makes a 23° angle with the ground. What is the value of *y*?

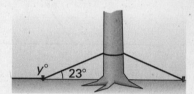

**LESSON 9.2** **Practice**
For use with pages 468–472

**In Exercises 1–4, refer to the diagram.**

1. Name all pairs of adjacent, supplementary angles.

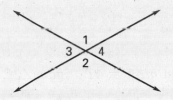

2. Name all pairs of vertical angles.

3. Given that $m\angle 1 = 123°$, find $m\angle 4$.

4. Given that $m\angle 1 = 123°$, find $m\angle 2$.

**Tell whether the dark lines appear to be *parallel*, *perpendicular*, or *neither*.**

5.

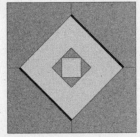

6.

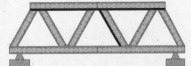

7.

**Scaffolding is used by builders to safely work on tall structures. In Exercises 8–11, use the figure of the scaffolding.**

8. Name all pairs of adjacent, supplementary angles.

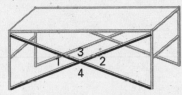

9. Name all pairs of vertical angles.

**LESSON**
**9.2**

# Practice continued
For use with pages 468–472

**10.** Given that $m\angle 1 = 42°$, find $m\angle 4$.

**11.** Given that $m\angle 1 = 42°$, find $m\angle 2$.

## In Exercises 12–17, refer to the street map.

**12.** Find $m\angle 1$.

**13.** Find $m\angle 2$.

**14.** Find $m\angle 3$.

**15.** Find $m\angle 4$.

**16.** Find $m\angle 5$.

**17.** Find $m\angle 6$.

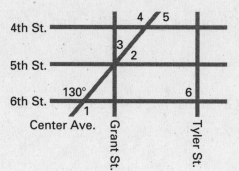

Name _____     Date _____

**Find the value of x in the triangle shown.**

**1.**
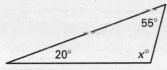

**2.**
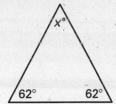

**3.**
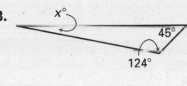

**The measures of two of the angles in a triangle are given.**
**Find the measure of the third angle.**

  **4.** 126.5° and 19°      **5.** 65.5° and 85°      **6.** 110.3° and 35.7°

**Classify the triangle by its angle measures.**

  **7.** 43°, 47°, 90°      **8.** 46°, 78°, 56°      **9.** 62°, 23°, 95°

**Classify the triangle by the lengths of its sides.**

**10.**
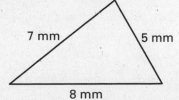

**11.**
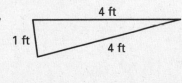

**12.**
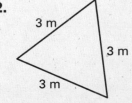

**Draw the triangle using a protractor and a ruler.**

**13.** An acute isosceles triangle with one angle measure of 45°

**14.** A right triangle with one angle measure of 30°

Lesson 9.3

**LESSON 9.3**

# Practice *continued*
For use with pages 473–479

**15.** An obtuse scalene triangle with one angle measure of 110°

**16.** The national flag of the Bahamas is shown at the right. Classify the triangle in the flag by its angle measures.

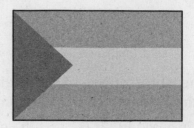

**17.** A roof truss is used to support the roof of a house. Find the value of *y*.

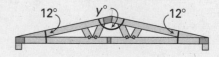

*Lesson 9.3*

**LESSON**
**9.4**

# Practice
For use with pages 482–488

**Use the clues to sketch and classify the quadrilateral described.**

1. This figure has four sides each with length 30 millimeters. Its opposite sides are parallel. Not all of the angles are congruent.

2. This figure's opposite sides are parallel with one side of length 4 centimeters and another side of length 5 centimeters. This figure has four right angles.

**Find the value of x.**

3.

4.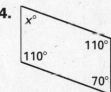

5.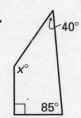

**Classify the polygon and tell if it is regular. If it is not regular, explain why not.**

6.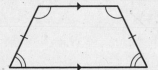

7.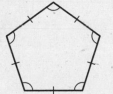

8.

**LESSON 9.4**

# Practice *continued*
For use with pages 482–488

9.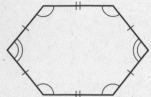

10.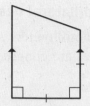

11.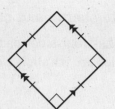

12. Graph and connect the ordered pairs (6, 6), (6, 4), (4, 2), (2, 4), (2, 6), and (6, 6) in the order they are given. Classify the polygon and tell if it is regular. If it is not regular, explain why not.

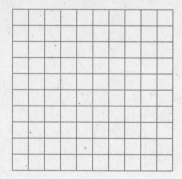

13. The front of the birdhouse shown is a regular pentagon. Find the perimeter of the front of the birdhouse.

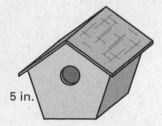

5 in.

14. The stop sign shown is a regular octagon. Find the sum of the angle measures in the stop sign.

**LESSON 9.5** **Practice**
For use with pages 489–494

**Name the corresponding sides and the corresponding angles of the congruent polygons. Then find the unknown measures.**

**1.** $RSTU \cong WXYZ$

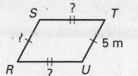
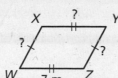

**2.** $\triangle DEF \cong \triangle GHI$

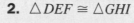
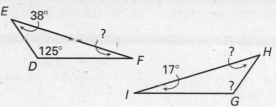

**Tell whether the two polygons are similar. If they are similar, find the ratio of the lengths of the corresponding sides of figure A to figure B.**

**3.**

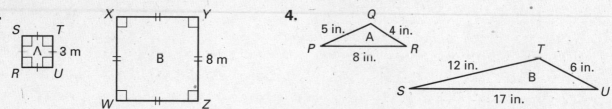

**4.**

**5.**

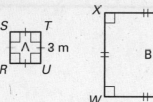

**6.**

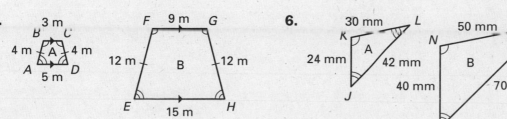
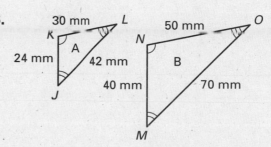

Name —————————————————————————————— Date ———————————————

7. A kite is shown in the figure at the right. Name the corresponding sides and the corresponding angles of the congruent triangles △*ABD* and △*CBD*. Then find the unknown measures.

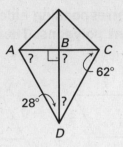

8. The cover of your math book is 11 inches long and 8 inches wide. The cover of your history book is 9 inches long and 7 inches wide. Are the covers similar figures?

# Practice
For use with pages 495–499

**1.** Describe and correct the error in finding the unknown length x in the similar polygons.

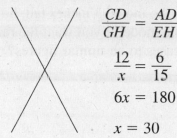

$$\frac{CD}{GH} = \frac{AD}{EH}$$

$$\frac{12}{x} = \frac{6}{15}$$

$$6x = 180$$

$$x = 30$$

**Find the unknown length x given that the polygons are similar.**

**2.**

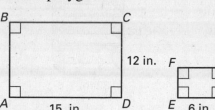

**3.**

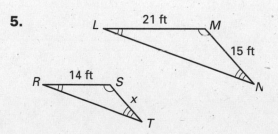

**4.**

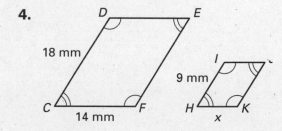

**5.**

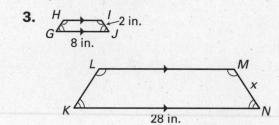

**6.**

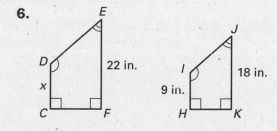

**7.**

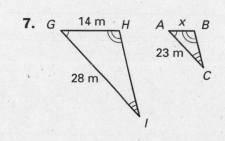

## LESSON 9.6 | **Practice**
For use with pages 495–499

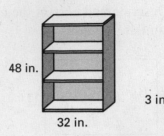

8. You are creating a model of a bookcase for a dollhouse.
The actual bookcase is 48 inches tall and 32 inches wide.
If you plan to make the model 3 inches tall, how wide do
you have to make the model if you want the rectangular
shapes of the bookcases to be similar figures?

48 in.

32 in.

3 in.

?

9. A person who is 6 feet tall stands next to a tree and casts a shadow
that is 2 feet long. At the same time, the shadow of the tree is 6 feet
long. How tall is the tree?

*Lesson 9.6*

Name _____    Date _____

Lesson 10.1

**Match the measures that are equivalent.**

**1.** 72.3 km                          **A.** 0.000723 km

**2.** 0.0723 m                         **B.** 72,300 m

**3.** 0.723 cm                         **C.** 7.23 cm

**4.** 723 mm                           **D.** 7.23 mm

**Complete the statement.**

**5.** To convert from milliliters to __?__, you divide by 1000.

**6.** To convert from grams to __?__, you multiply by 100.

**7.** To convert from centimeters to __?__, you divide by 100,000.

**Complete the statement.**

**8.** 2.56 g = __?__ mg                 **9.** 2614 m = __?__ km

**10.** 0.56 L = __?__ mL               **11.** 250,000 mg = __?__ g

**12.** 18 m = __?__ cm                 **13.** 7.14 kg = __?__ g

**LESSON
10.1**  **Practice** *continued*
For use with pages 515–519

**14.** 394 cm = __?__ m

**15.** 1.405 km = __?__ m

**16.** 41,250 mL = __?__ L

**Complete the statement using <, >, or =.**

**17.** 420 mm __?__ 4.2 cm

**18.** 5600 mg __?__ 56 g

**19.** 21,480 mL __?__ 214.8 L

**20.** 6.24 m __?__ 624 cm

**21.** 4.02 kL __?__ 40,200,000 mL

**22.** 14 kg __?__ 14,000 mg

**23.** Describe and correct the error in
converting 0.85 liters to milliliters.

0.85 ÷ 1000 = 0.00085

So, 0.85 L = 0.00085 mL.

**24.** A bookcase is 1.98 meters tall and its shelves are 33 centimeters apart.
How many shelves are in the bookcase?

**25.** One can of juice contains 335 milliliters of liquid. How many liters of
liquid are in a 12-pack of juice?

**26.** The bee hummingbird, the world's smallest bird, is only 6.3 centimeters
long. The ostrich, one of the world's tallest birds, can reach a height of
2.5 meters. How much longer, in centimeters, is the ostrich than the bee
hummingbird?

Lesson 10.1

**LESSON 10.2**  **Practice**
For use with pages 520–525

**Complete the statement.**

**1.** $7\frac{1}{3}$ yd $-$ __?__ ft

**2.** $5\frac{1}{2}$ T $=$ __?__ lb

**3.** $9\frac{3}{4}$ qt $=$ __?__ pt

**4.** 15,840 ft $=$ __?__ mi

**5.** 20 oz $=$ __?__ lb

**6.** $10\frac{2}{3}$ c $=$ __?__ pt

**7.** 78 in. $=$ __?__ yd

**8.** 30 fl oz $=$ __?__ c __?__ fl oz

**9.** 50 fl oz $=$ __?__ c __?__ fl oz

**Find the sum or difference.**

**10.**    7 yd  4 ft
      $+$ 9 yd  2 ft

**11.**     5 lb  9 oz
      $+$ 17 lb  9 oz

**12.**     8 c  3 fl oz
      $-$ 3 c  6 fl oz

**Complete the statement using, $<$, $>$ or $=$.**

**13.** $5\frac{2}{3}$ ft __?__ 65 in.

**14.** $1\frac{3}{4}$ lb __?__ 25 oz

**15.** $3\frac{1}{2}$ c __?__ 28 fl oz

**16.** 4000 ft __?__ $\frac{3}{4}$ mi

**17.** $5\frac{3}{5}$ lb __?__ 92 oz

**18.** $\frac{3}{4}$ gal __?__ 6 pt

**19.** Describe and correct the error in converting $5\frac{1}{3}$ cups to quarts.

$$5\frac{1}{3} \text{ c} = \frac{16 \text{ c}}{3} \times \frac{2 \text{ pt}}{1 \text{ c}} \times \frac{1 \text{ qt}}{2 \text{ pt}} \times \frac{16}{3} \text{ qt} = 5\frac{1}{3} \text{ qt}$$

**Practice** *continued*
For use with pages 520–525

## Order the measurements from least to greatest.

**20.** $5\frac{1}{2}$ ft, $1\frac{2}{3}$ yd, 69 in., 5 ft 3 in.          **21.** $7\frac{1}{3}$ c, 58 fl oz, $3\frac{1}{4}$ pt, 60 fl oz

**22.** A recipe for caesar dressing calls for $\frac{3}{4}$ cup of olive oil. Convert the
amount of olive oil to fluid ounces.

**23.** The names of three longest suspension bridges in the United States
and their lengths are shown below. Determine which bridge is the
longest.

| Bridge | Golden Gate | Mackinac Straits | Verrazano-Narrows |
|--------|-------------|------------------|-------------------|
| Length | 1400 yds | 3800 ft | 51,120 in. |

Lesson 10.2

**LESSON 10.3** **Practice**
For use with pages 527–531

## Copy and complete the statement. Round to the nearest whole number.

**1.** 15 m = __?__ ft

**2.** 28.5 g ≈ __?__ oz

**3.** 26 gal ≈ __?__ L

**4.** 50 in. = __?__ cm

**5.** 7 fl oz ≈ __?__ mL

**6.** 21 km ≈ __?__ mi

**7.** 37 qt ≈ __?__ L

**8.** 35 kg ≈ __?__ lb

**9.** 18 cm = __?__ in.

## Copy and complete using $<$, $>$, or $=$.

**10.** 40 ft __?__ 10 m

**11.** 150 L __?__ 50 gal

**12.** 20 lb __?__ 10 kg

**13.** 25 in. __?__ 63.5 cm

**14.** 60 km __?__ 35 mi

**15.** 40 L __?__ 44 qt

**16.** Describe and correct the error made in converting 10 liters to gallons.

$$10\ L \times \frac{1\ gal}{0.946\ L} \approx 10.57\ gal$$
10 Liters is about 11 gallons. ✕

**LESSON
10.3** **Practice** *continued*
For use with pages 527–531

**Copy and complete the statement using the exchange rate 1
U.S. dollar ≈ 10.825 Mexican pesos. Round to the nearest whole
number.**

**17.** 25 U.S. dollars ≈ __?__ Mexican pesos      **18.** 150 Mexican pesos ≈ __?__ U.S. dollars

**19.** 100 Mexican pesos ≈ __?__ U.S. dollars      **20.** 75 U.S. dollars ≈ __?__ Mexican pesos

**21.** A long jump competition is held at a track meet. The participant
with the longest jump is the winner. Which participant is the winner?

| Participant | Jose | Mike | Alfonos | Juan |
|---|---|---|---|---|
| Length | 7 ft | 72 in. | 198 cm | 2.3 m |

**22.** The wingspan of a Canadian goose is 5 feet. Find the length (in
centimeters) of the goose's wingspan. Round to the nearest whole
number.

Lesson 10.3

Name _____   Date _____

**Find the area of the parallelogram.**

1.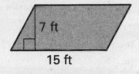
   7 ft
   15 ft

2.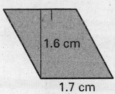
   1.6 cm
   1.7 cm

3.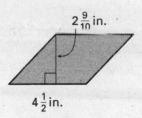
   $2\frac{9}{10}$ in.
   $4\frac{1}{2}$ in.

**Find the unknown base or height of the parallelogram.**

4. $A = 63 \text{ m}^2, b = 7 \text{ m}, h = \underline{\quad?\quad}$

5. $A = 180 \text{ yd}^2, b = \underline{\quad?\quad}, h = 15 \text{ yd}$

6. $A = 42 \text{ mm}^2, b = \underline{\quad?\quad}, h = 12 \text{ mm}$

7. $A = 16 \text{ ft}^2, b = \frac{2}{3} \text{ ft}, h = \underline{\quad?\quad}$

8. Describe and correct the error in finding the area of the parallelogram.

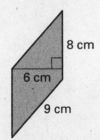
8 cm
6 cm
9 cm

$A = bh$
$= 8 \times 9$
$= 72$

The area of the parallelogram is 72 square centimeters.

**LESSON 10.4** **Practice** *continued*
For use with pages 533–538

**Write an expression that represents the area of the shaded region in terms of *x*.**

9.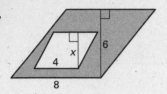

10.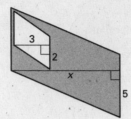

11.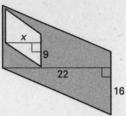

12. The base and height of a parallelogram in a floor tile pattern are 4.5 inches and 3 inches, respectively. What is the area of the piece of tile?

Name _____  Date _____

**LESSON 10.5** **Practice**
For use with pages 539–546

CA Standards
AF 3.1
AF 3.2

**Find the area of the triangle.**

1.
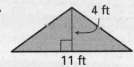
4 ft
11 ft

2.
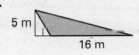
5 m
16 m

3.
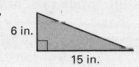
6 in.
15 in.

**Find the unknown base or height of the triangle.**

4. $A = 56 \text{ km}^2, b = \underline{\ ?\ }, h = 8 \text{ km}$

5. $A = 25.5 \text{ mm}^2, b = 3 \text{ mm}, h = \underline{\ ?\ }$

6. $A = 42 \text{ mi}^2, b = 7 \text{ mi}, h = \underline{\ ?\ }$

7. $A = 88 \text{ ft}^2, b = \underline{\ ?\ }, h = 8 \text{ ft}$

**Find the area of the trapezoid.**

8.
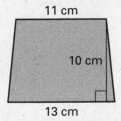
11 cm
10 cm
13 cm

9.
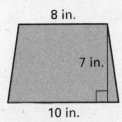
8 in.
7 in.
10 in.

10.
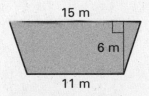
15 m
6 m
11 m

**Write an expression for the area of the triangle or trapezoid in terms of x.**

11.
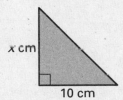
$x$ cm
10 cm

12.
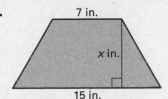
7 in.
$x$ in.
15 in.

13.
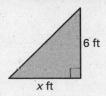
6 ft
$x$ ft

**LESSON 10.5** **Practice** *continued*
For use with pages 539–546

**14.** A truss for a roof is shown in the figure.
What is the total area enclosed by the truss?

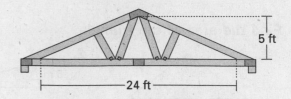

5 ft

24 ft

**15.** A bridge design used for a model railroad is
shown in the figure. What is the area enclosed
by the trapezoid that makes up the bridge?

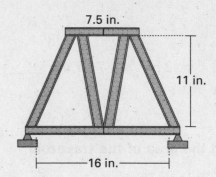

7.5 in.

11 in.

16 in.

Name _____     Date _____

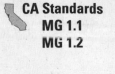

**Match the radius or diameter of a circle with the circle's circumference.**

**1.** $r = 16$ in.          **2.** $d = 8$ in.          **3.** $r = 8$ in.

**A.** $C = 8\pi$ in.          **B.** $C = 16\pi$ in.          **C.** $C = 32\pi$ in.

**Find the circumference of the circle. Use $\frac{22}{7}$ or 3.14 for $\pi$.**

**4.**
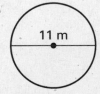
11 m

**5.**

9 ft

**6.**

3.5 cm

**7.**

24 yd

**8.**
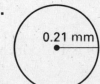
0.21 mm

**9.**

15 m

**Find the circumference of the circle in terms of $\pi$.**

**10.**

4 in.

**11.**

7 m

**12.**

10 ft

**LESSON**
**10.6**

# Practice *continued*
For use with pages 547–554

*Lesson 10.6*

**Find the diameter and the radius of the circle with the given circumference. Use $\frac{22}{7}$ or 3.14 for $\pi$.**

**13.** $C = 25.12$ in.

**14.** $C = 69.08$ m

**15.** $C = 100.48$ mm

**16.** $C = 32.97$ km

**17.** $C = 4\frac{2}{5}$ cm

**18.** $C = 16.328$ ft

**19.** Automobile tires are mounted on circular metal rims. If a tire rim has a 13-inch diameter, what is its circumference?

**20.** Rings are made in sizes that can range from 0 to 13. A size 6 ring has an inside diameter of 16.51 millimeters. What is the inside circumference of the ring?

16.51 mm

**21.** The circumference of a candlepin bowling ball is 14.13 inches. What is the diameter of the bowling ball?

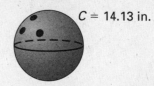
$C = 14.13$ in.

Name _____    Date _____

# Practice

For use with pages 555–559

**Find the area of the circle. Use 3.14 for $\pi$.**

**1.**
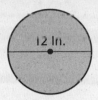
12 in.

**2.**

5.2 cm

**3.**
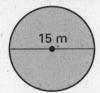
9 yd

**4.**
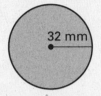
32 mm

**5.**

6.24 ft

**6.**
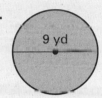
15 m

**Find the area of the circle with the given radius $r$ or diameter $d$.**
**Write your answer in terms of $\pi$.**

**7.** $r = 13$ m

**8.** $d = 7$ cm

**9.** $r = 4.7$ ft

**10.** $d = 3$ in.

**11.** $r = 27$ yd

**12.** $d = 17$ mm

**13.** Describe and correct the error in finding
the area of a circle with a diameter
of 3.5 inches.

$A = \pi r^2$
$\approx (3.14)(3.5)^2$
$= 38.465$ in.$^2$

# Practice continued
For use with pages 555–559

**Lesson 10.7**

**Find the area of the circle with the given circumference. Use 3.14 for $\pi$.**

**14.** $C = 31.4$ ft

**15.** $C = 69.08$ cm

**16.** $C = 17.27$ yd

**Complete the statement using <, >, or =.**

**17.** Area of a circle with a 5 foot radius ___?___ 75.5 ft$^2$

**18.** Area of a circle with a 16 inch diameter ___?___ 200.75 in.$^2$

**19.** Area of a circle with a 2.75 centimeter radius ___?___ 23.74625 cm$^2$

**20.** The center ice spot on an ice hockey rink is a circle with a 15-foot radius. What is the area and the circumference of the center ice spot?

**21.** A dinner plate has an 11-inch diameter and a salad plate has an 8-inch diameter. How many more square inches does the dinner plate cover than the salad plate?

Name _____  Date _____

**Practice**
For use with pages 575–579

CA Standards
Gr. 5 MG 2.3

**Classify the solid represented by the object. Be as specific as possible.**

1.

2.

3.

4.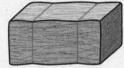

5.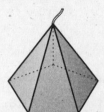

6.

**Match the view with its solid.**

7. The front view of the solid is a rectangle.

8. The top view of the solid is a square.

9. The front view of the solid is a triangle.

A.

B.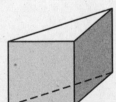

C.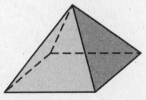

**Sketch the top, side, and front views of the solid.**

10.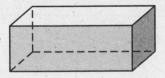

11.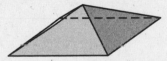

**LESSON 11.1** **Practice** *continued*
For use with pages 575–579

**Lesson 11.1**

### Sketch the top, side, and front views of the solid.

12.

13.

### Draw the top, side, and front views of the solid.

14.

15.

16.

Name _____  Date _____

**Draw a net for the rectangular prism. Then use the net to find the surface area of the prism.**

**1.**

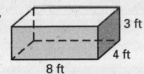

3 ft
4 ft
8 ft

**2.**

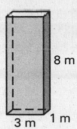

8 m
3 m   1 m

**3.**

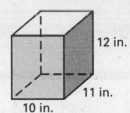

12 in.
11 in.
10 in.

**4.** Describe and correct the error in finding the surface area of the rectangular prism.

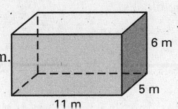

6 m
5 m
11 m

$S = 11(5) + 11(6) + 5(6)$
$\quad = 55 + 66 + 30$
$\quad = 151 \text{ m}^2$

**Find the surface area of the rectangular prism.**

**5.**

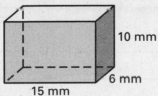

10 mm
6 mm
15 mm

**6.**

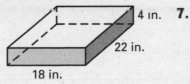

4 in.
22 in.
18 in.

**7.**

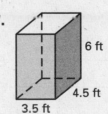

6 ft
4.5 ft
3.5 ft

Lesson 11.2

# Practice *continued*
For use with pages 580–586

**8.**
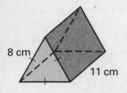
8 cm

11 cm

**9.**
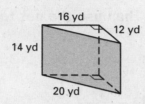
16 yd

12 yd

14 yd

20 yd

**10.**
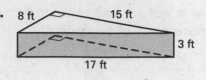
8 ft          15 ft

3 ft

17 ft

**11.** You are making a set of 12 wooden building blocks for your brother. Six of the blocks will be 2 inches long, 2 inches wide, and 2 inches high. The other six blocks will be 4 inches long, 3 inches wide, and 1 inch high. Find the total surface area of the wooden blocks so you can buy enough paint to cover the blocks.

**12.** You decide to make four more wooden building blocks in the shape of triangular prisms. The rectangular faces of the triangular prisms each have a length of 3 inches and a width of 2 inches. The area of a base is about 1.7 square inches. How much paint will you need to cover these four blocks?

Name _____   Date _____

Draw a net for the cylinder and label the dimensions. Then use
the net to find the surface area of the cylinder. Use 3.14 for π.

1.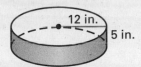

2.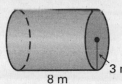

3.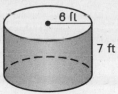

Find the surface area of the cylindrical object. Use 3.14 for π.

4.

5.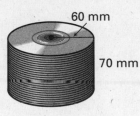

6.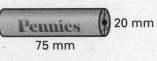

Find the surface area of a cylinder with the given dimensions.
Use 3.14 for π. Write your answer using the smaller unit.

7. Radius: 2 cm
   Height: 5 mm

8. Radius: 3 in.
   Height: 4 ft

9. Radius: 12 cm
   Height: 1 m

Lesson 11.3

**LESSON
11.3**   ## Practice *continued*
For use with pages 588–593

**10.** The barrel of a rolling pin has a diameter of 8 centimeters and
a length of 25 centimeters. What is the surface area of the barrel?

**11.** You are decorating the hat box shown. If you cover all but the
bottom of the box in fabric, how much fabric do you need?

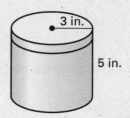

**12.** A soup can has a diameter of 80 millimeters and a height
of 125 millimeters. What is the surface area of the soup can?

**13.** A builder is painting the support columns for the front porch of a house before they are
installed. There are four columns and they are each 15 feet tall and 4 feet in diameter. How
much paint do you need to completely cover all four columns with one coat of paint?

## LESSON 11.4 Practice

For use with pages 595–600

**Find the volume of the prism.**

**1.**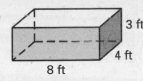

**2.**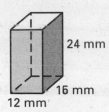

**3.**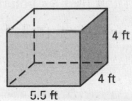

**4.**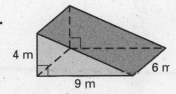

**5.**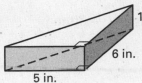

**6.**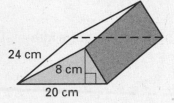

**Find the height of the rectangular prism.**

**7.** $V = 120 \text{ mm}^3$
$\ell - 5 \text{ mm}$
$w = 8 \text{ mm}$
$h = \underline{\quad}$

**8.** $V = 720 \text{ ft}^3$
$\ell = 10 \text{ ft}$
$w = 8 \text{ ft}$
$h = \underline{\quad}$

**9.** $V = 1500 \text{ cm}^3$
$\ell = 15 \text{ cm}$
$w = 20 \text{ cm}$
$h = \underline{\quad}$

**LESSON 11.4** **Practice** *continued*
For use with pages 595–600

**Make a sketch of the rectangular prism with the given dimensions. Then find its volume.**

**10.** length = 2 in., width = 2 in., height = 3 in.

**11.** length = 5 cm, width = 6 cm, height = 7 cm

**12.** length = 40 mm, width = 45 mm, height = 30 mm

**13.** Find the volume of the aquarium shown.

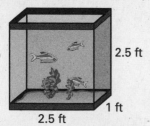

2.5 ft
1 ft
2.5 ft

**14.** You are building the steps shown below. How many cubic inches of concrete will you need to make the steps?

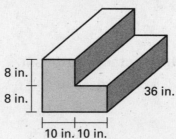

8 in.
8 in.
36 in.
10 in. 10 in.

Lesson 11.4

Name _____

Date _____

**LESSON 11.5** **Practice**
For use with pages 601–606

**Find the volume of the cylinder. Use 3.14 for $\pi$.**

**1.**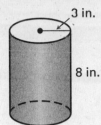
3 in.
8 in.

**2.**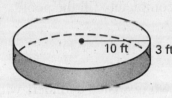
10 ft
3 ft

**3.**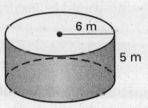
6 m
5 m

**4.** Describe and correct the error in finding the volume of the cylinder.

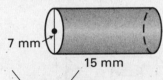
7 mm
15 mm

$V = \pi r^2 h$

$\approx (3.14)(7)^2(15)$

$= 2307.9 \text{ mm}^3$

**Tell which cylinder has the greater volume.**

**5.** Cylinder A: $r = 5$ ft, $h = 12$ ft; Cylinder B: $r = 7$ ft, $h = 10$ ft

**6.** Cylinder C: $r = 20$ cm, $h = 15$ cm; Cylinder D: $r = 22$ cm, $h = 14.5$ cm

**Find the unknown height of the cylinder. Use 3.14 for $\pi$.**

**7.** $V = 628$ in.$^3$
$r = 5$ in.
$h = $ ___?___

**8.** $V = 565.2$ m$^3$
$r = 3$ m
$h = $ ___?___

**9.** $V = 3925$ ft$^3$
$d = 10$ ft
$h = $ ___?___

Name ———————————————————————— Date ————————————

**10.** A swimming pool is 3 feet deep and has a diameter of 12 feet. How much water would be needed to completely fill the pool?

**11.** For a hiking trip, you are filling two insulated cylinders with soup. If one cylinder has a diameter of 5 inches and a height of 9 inches and the other cylinder has a diameter of 4.5 inches and a height of 12 inches, how much soup can you take for the trip?

**Write an expression for the volume of the solid.**

**12.**

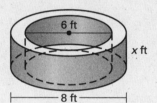

**13.**

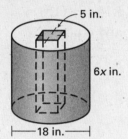

**14.**

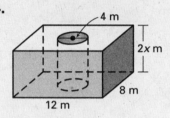

Name _____ Date _____

**Name the ordered pair that describes the point.**

**1.** *A*

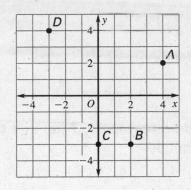

**2.** *B*

**3.** *C*

**4.** *D*

**Name the ordered pair that is described by the action.**

**5.** Point *E* is located 5 units to the left of the origin and 5 units above the origin.

**6.** Point *F* is located 6 units to the right of the origin and 3 units below the origin.

**Plot the point and describe its location.**

**7.** *G*(4, −5)          **8.** *H*(−3, −2)          **9.** *I*(−4, 0)

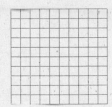  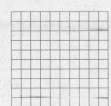

**LESSON 12.1**

# Practice *continued*
For use with pages 623–629

*Lesson 12.1*

**10.** $J(-1, 2)$

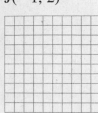

**11.** $K(0, 2)$

**12.** $L(3, 3)$

**Plot and connect the points to form a rectangle. Then find the length, width, and area of the rectangle.**

**13.** $A(0, 0), B(3, 0), C(3, 4), D(0, 4)$

**14.** $W(-1, -1), X(-1, 3), Y(4, 3), Z(4, -1)$

**15.** Make a conclusion about the scatter plot.

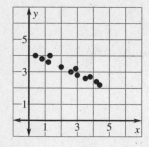

**16.** The ordered pairs show the heights, in inches, and the weights, in pounds, of seven American Quarter Horses. Make a scatter plot of the data. Then make a conclusion about the data.

(60.3, 950), (60.8, 1100), (60.5, 980), (61.7, 1200), (63.8, 1190), (61.4, 980), (62.6, 1140)

**17.** Using your results from Exercise 16, predict the weight of an American Quarter Horse that is 62 inches tall.

**LESSON 12.2** **Practice**
For use with pages 630–634

CA Standards
Gr 5 AF 1.5

**Evaluate the function $y = 5x - 3$ for the given value of $x$.**

**1.** 7                **2.** 0                **3.** $-4$

**Match the function with its possible range.**

**4.** $y = 2x - 1$          **A.** $-7, -4, -1, 2, 5, 8$

**5.** $y = -x + 2$          **B.** $-5, -3, -1, 1, 3$

**6.** $y = 3x - 1$          **C.** $11, 6, 1, -4, -9, -14$

**7.** $y = -5x + 1$         **D.** $4, 3, 2, 1, 0$

**Make an input-output table for the function using the domain $-2, -1, 0, 1,$ and 2. Then state the range of the function.**

**8.** $y = x + 8$          **9.** $y = -15x$          **10.** $y = 4x$

**11.** $y = x - 3$          **12.** $y = 2x - 3$          **13.** $y = 18 - 3x$

**LESSON 12.2**

# Practice *continued*

For use with pages 630–634

**Write a function rule for the input-output table.**

**14.**

| Input $x$ | 0 | 1 | 2 | 3 |
|---|---|---|---|---|
| Output $y$ | 3 | 4 | 5 | 6 |

**15.**

| Input $x$ | 0 | 1 | 2 | 3 |
|---|---|---|---|---|
| Output $y$ | 5 | 4 | 3 | 2 |

**16.**

| Input $x$ | −3 | −2 | −1 | 0 |
|---|---|---|---|---|
| Output $y$ | −12 | −8 | −4 | 0 |

**17.**

| Input $x$ | 0 | 1 | 2 | 3 |
|---|---|---|---|---|
| Output $y$ | 1 | 3 | 5 | 7 |

**18.** A custom case company makes travel cases for computer equipment. There is a 2-inch foam lining around the inside of each case. The function $y = x + 4$, where $x$ is the width of a laptop computer, can be used to find the total width of a laptop case, including the foam lining. Create an input-output table using the domain 12, 15, 18, and 21.

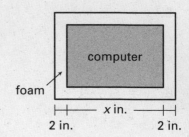

**19.** A magazine costs $5 per issue. Write a function rule that models the cost $y$ of $x$ issues. Then use the function to calculate the cost of 6 issues.

**20.** It costs 15 pennies to make one copy on the copier at the local library. Write a function rule that models the cost $y$ of making $x$ copies. Then use the function to calculate the cost of 24 copies.

**LESSON 12.3** **Practice**
For use with pages 636–641

**Identify the graph of the function on the coordinate plane.**

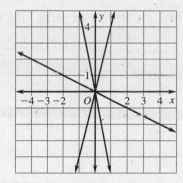

**1.** $y = -5x$

**2.** $y = 4x$

**3.** $y = -\frac{1}{2}x$

**Graph the function.**

**4.** $y = 3x$

**5.** $y = 8 - x$

**6.** $y = \frac{1}{4}x$

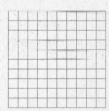

**7.** $y = x + 5$

**8.** $y = 3x - 6$

**9.** $y = -2x + 3$

**10.** $y = \frac{1}{3}x + 2$

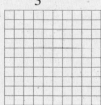

**11.** $y = 0.75x - 3$

**12.** $y = -x - 8$

**LESSON**
**12.3**

**Practice** *continued*
For use with pages 636–641

**Write and graph a function that converts the units.**

**13.** $x$ feet to $y$ inches

**14.** $x$ pounds to $y$ ounces

**15.** $x$ months to $y$ years

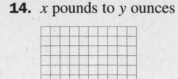

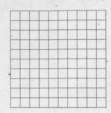

**16.** When you are swimming, your body burns about 8 calories every minute. Write and graph a function that models the number of calories burned $y$ after swimming for $x$ minutes.

**17.** Outdoor carpeting costs $1.25 for each square foot. Write and graph a function that models the cost $y$ of $x$ square feet of carpeting.

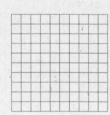

**18.** A phone company charges a $.25 dialing fee for calling a long-distance number and then charges $.10 for each minute of the call. This situation can be represented by the function $y = 0.1x + 0.25$, where $y$ is the total cost of the call and $x$ is the length of the call in minutes. Graph the function.

Name _____ Date _____

**Without finding the slope of the line, tell whether the slope is positive, negative, or zero.**

1.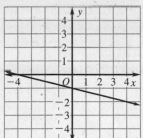

2.

3.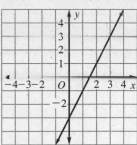

**Find the slope of the line.**

4.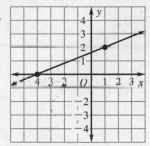

5.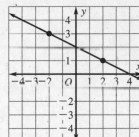

6.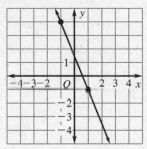

**Draw the graph of the line that passes through the points. Then find the slope of the line.**

7. $(4, 1), (5, 2)$

8. $(0, 0), (3, -4)$

9. $(-2, 5), (1, -2)$

**LESSON 12.4** **Practice** *continued*
For use with pages 642–647

**10.** $(-3, -1), (2, -4)$

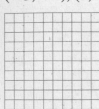

**11.** $(5, 1), (-2, 2)$

**12.** $(-2, 3), (-5, -2)$

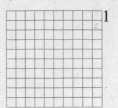

**Draw the line that has the given slope and passes through the given point.**

**13.** slope $= 2$; $(-4, 1)$

**14.** slope $= \frac{2}{3}$; $(4, 1)$

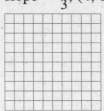

**15.** slope $= -\frac{1}{2}$; $(0, 3)$

**In Exercises 16–18, use the graph that shows the 2001 state gasoline tax rates for Alabama and Colorado.**

**16.** Find Alabama's gasoline tax rate in cents per gallon.

**17.** Find Colorado's gasoline tax rate in cents per gallon.

**18.** Which state had a higher gasoline tax rate?

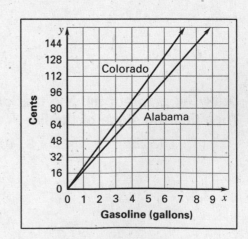